COMBAT AND SURVIVAL
WHAT IT TAKES TO FIGHT AND WIN

VOLUME
10

Originally published in the United Kingdom in weekly parts **COMBAT & SURVIVAL** is a study of the armed forces at work. It shows the skills taught to soldiers and the way in which military units operate. It examines the weapons and equipment used by different armies; and, by looking at recruit training and exercises, **COMBAT & SURVIVAL** demonstrates how the armed forces develop individual responsibility, leadership and initiative.

COMBAT AND SURVIVAL

WHAT IT TAKES TO FIGHT AND WIN

VOLUME
10

H. S. STUTTMAN INC. *Publishers*   Westport, Connecticut 06880

Contents

Volume 10

Published by H. S. STUTTMAN INC.
Westport, Connecticut 06889
© Aerospace Publishing 1991
ISBN 0-87475-560-3

4P(2295)20-90

Combat Skills

KILLING TANKS

Enemy tanks, infantry fighting vehicles and other hostile armour represent probably the greatest threat you'll face when defending your position on the European battlefield. This threat more than anything else will dictate how you set out your defences.

A Soviet T-62 emerges from a blazing forest, its stabilised 115-mm gun ready for the next target. As an infantryman, the tank is still your most feared enemy and unless you co-ordinate your anti-tank weapons it can smash your defences in minutes.

But preparing to defeat an armoured attack doesn't mean that you should slip into a defensive state of mind. Your tactics should be aggressive, imaginative and effective. This is when the enemy is at his most stretched and his most vulnerable – and you have a golden opportunity to inflict massive tank casualties on him.

Use your ground

Use natural obstacles to hinder and impede the enemy, and to canalise his approach – that is, make him travel

5 POINTS FOR TANK-KILLING

1. Choose a firing position where you are firing into the side of enemy tanks but protected and concealed from the direction of enemy approach.
2. Camouflage your position well, and use at least 45 cm of overhead protection over the weapon position.
3. Fire in support of the anti-tank weapons to your right and left; you should also be able to cover most, if not all, of the ground they cover.
4. Use mines and obstacles to channel the tanks into an area ideal for you to engage them in.
5. Choose your target carefully; concentrate on command tanks and the ZSU 23-4, which provides air defence.

The Dragon system is currently in service with the US Army. The gunner just keeps the crosshairs of the sight on the target, and the tracker automatically guides the missile along the gunner's line of sight.

Milan is a man-portable system (just); the two-man team comprises the gunner, who manhandles the firing post and fires the weapon, and the No. 2, who carries two rockets and loads them on the firing post. Each rocket weighs 11.3 kg and the firing post 16.5 kg.

along the lines you want, to where you can ambush, harass or destroy him at will.

Remember that armoured vehicles are very limited by the ground that they can use. They need bridging or snorkelling equipment to cross anything but the smallest rivers or streams. Marshy or swampy ground is impassable to main battle tanks, and close or wooded country, if not impassable, gives you an opportunity for tank ambush at close range.

Similarly, built-up areas delay and channel the movement of armoured vehicles and make them vulnerable to close-range infantry anti-tank weapons. You can of course thicken up all these natural anti-tank obstacles with minefields and, if you are defending a built-up area, with rub-

ble, overturned buses and any other sort of artificial obstacle.

Use surprise

You can use 'dead' ground to conceal your defending, reserve and counter-attack forces. You can sight your anti-tank weapons in defilade positions (hidden from frontal observation) in order to provide enfilade fire (from a flank). You will then surprise the enemy from a flank and hit him where his armour is thinnest. The tank is also a bigger and easier target in enfilade.

You can also use reverse slopes. In other words, sight your anti-tank weapons several hundred yards back from the crest of a ridge or hill: your positions are then invisible to the enemy until he crosses the crest. You

Fighter ground attack
As well as Lynx anti-tank helicopters, there may be ground attack aircraft such as the A-10 or Harrier GR.Mk 3 available for tank-busting.

Priority target
Warsaw Pact radio procedure is very strictly controlled: only battalion or company commanders are allowed to speak! Everyone else simply maintains a listening watch and passes no information, so if a command tank is knocked out then confusion reigns.

Counter-mobility
The engineers can create anti-tank obstacles or improve existing natural obstacles to further channel the enemy into the killing zone.

Reverse slope positions
Always consider a reverse slope position first. Not only does it provide a degree of protection from direct and indirect fire, but it also gives a better chance of preserving surprise. But you will need OPs forward to provide adequate warning of enemy approach.

84-mm MAW
An old but extremely solid piece of kit, there are moves to retain it with an improved ammunition while the new 80-mm LAW is perfected. The 84 has a massive blast signature and is almost as impressive at the firing end as it is on the receiving end. If there is time, it is well worth digging secondary, alternative positions and perhaps dummy positions. The essential thing is, you can't afford to miss very often!

Wombat is a 120-mm recoilless rifle still in use by the British Army's Berlin garrison and some Territorial Army units. Although it cannot match the Milan's excellent tank-killing capability, it remains a very worthwhile tool for fighting in built-up areas.

66-mm LAW
Great for short-range work on BMPs, BTR-60s etc, LAW could be used against tanks in a desperate situation. If you are taking on a tank with this weapon, fire volleys rather than one shot after another; you are bound to get at least one round on target.

Mines
There are four types of minefield: the tactical large-area minefield, usually laid by the engineers, for tactical use on the battlefield (i.e. to canalise the enemy into killing areas); the protective minefield, the sort that you will plant in front of your position for defensive purposes; the nuisance minefield, designed to hamper and disrupt enemy movement; and the dummy minefield – a wired-off area suitably marked can be as effective as the real thing.

will have been safe from his long-range tank fire but, as he shows his belly when he crosses the ridgeline, you can engage him with maximum effect. Clever use of ground is probably the most effective counter to the tank threat.

Second, you must exploit to the full any conditions that favour you. Despite the most modern night-vision equipment, tanks are more vulnerable at night. Despite the most up-to-date thermal-imaging equipment, tanks are more vulnerable in poor visibility. Finally, tanks do not like either close country or built-up areas. Use these conditions when you can.

The weapon for the job

Well-planned and coordinated use of your anti-tank weapons will enable you to defeat enemy armour. In every battle group there is a combination of weapons systems for anti armour operations.

In the first category are hand-held infantry weapons: the 66-mm LAW, the 84-mm MAW and Milan anti-tank guided missile (ATGW) system.

The second category are the vehicle-mounted infantry anti-armour systems, the 30-mm Rarden Cannon mounted on the new Warrior APC or the Scimitar recce vehicle, and Milan mounted in the Milan Compact Turret (MCT) fitted to the Spartan APC.

In the third category are Royal Armoured Corps (RAC) anti-armour systems: these are the Swingfire ATGW mounted on Striker, the Rarden cannon mounted on Scimitar, the 76-mm gun mounted on Scorpion and, most important, the 120-mm main armament of Chieftain or Challenger – the most potent tank killer of all.

The fourth category consists of anti-tank mines laid by the Engineers: these are mostly designed to make a tank immobile, usually by blowing a track off.

The fifth category, and one that is showing enormous potential, is the anti-tank helicopter: in the British Army this is the versatile TOW/Lynx system, which is capable of firing eight TOW missiles out to 3,750 metres without reloading.

Big guns

The sixth category is artillery: large-calibre guns (155 mm and upwards) can be most effective against a massed

FIGHTING THE ANTI-ARMOUR BATTLE

Tanks combine firepower, mobility and armoured protection to produce what is known as 'shock action'. The quality and quantity of Warsaw Pact armour, combined with their massive indirect firepower capability, forms a serious threat, and with this in mind all defence on the NATO central front is designed around the anti-armour plan.

Chieftain
In positional defence, it is normal to fight in mixed teams of tanks and infantry with dedicated artillery support, as well as some signals and engineers. If you have tanks with you, then make sure the anti-tank plan is co-ordinated to include them. Each tank will have a number of fire positions pre-prepared, the idea being to fire two or three shots and move; this will give the tank a better chance of survival.

Small-arms fire
7.62-mm rifle and GPMG fire will force tanks to close down, making target acquisition more difficult. 0.50 calibre rounds will damage the BTR-60 and similar vehicles.

Weapons siting
In anti-tank warfare your siting of weapons is all-important to minimise your vulnerability to the enemy's direct and indirect fire.

Milan
Quick to deploy and devastating in positional defence, Milan would normally be fully dug in. The long flight time of the missile means you must be able to see the target for a full 12.5 seconds at maximum range, and the missile can be decoyed by other infra-red sources on the battlefield, like burning tank hulks. Milan must be deployed with short-range anti-tank protection (84-mm) and with infantry in a position to defend it.

Above: The 84-mm Carl Gustav anti-tank weapon is recoilless, operated by two men and fires an 84-mm HEAT round. It has a considerable backblast signature and there is some doubt whether it can defeat Soviet main battle tank frontal armour.

Right: The Milan system replaces the ageing 120-mm Wombat; it will defeat all known Soviet armour out to a range of 1950 metres. Again, it has a vicious backblast firing signature which affects survivability of the system.

Striker is a Spartan-armoured personnel carrier fitted with the Swingfire guided missile system. It will defeat any known armour combination from 150 to 4000 metres and is immune to electronic countermeasures.

tank attack. A concentrated artillery bombardment can ruin optics, destroy radio antennas, dislodge and set fire to external fuel tanks and disorient and disconcert tank crews. Multi-barrelled rocket systems such as MLRS can fire rockets that scatter bomblets designed to penetrate the weaker top armour of tanks. Ground attack aircraft such as the Harrier and A-10 are most effective tank destroyers: they are capable of either rocket or bomb attack against tank targets.

You will see from this brief gallop through the systems available to you, or in direct support of your battalion, that there is a vast array of weapon systems capable of defeating a tank attack. It is precisely because there are so many systems that they must be carefully coordinated in order to avoid duplication and waste.

Hands-on

Closest to you will be the hand-held weapons. They are designed for use under 1950 metres. Milan reaches out to this range, and the 84-mm MAW and 66-mm LAW reach to 600 and 350 metres respectively. Each system is designed to be used progressively as the enemy gets closer.

Milan is fitted with a Thermal Imaging system, so that you can use it 24 hours a day and in bad weather. Milan and the 84 mm/66 mm systems are complementary. You can use them to fill in gaps in the Milan defence, or you can use them to provide close anti-tank protection for isolated Milan crews or at distances below Milan's minimum range.

Weapons on wheels

In a mechanised battalion you will have your vehicles near you in your defensive position. Site them so that you can use their weapon systems to best advantage. Use the 30-mm Rarden cannon on Warrior and Scimitar to engage enemy APCs and other lightly armoured vehicles, and concentrate the firepower of tanks and long-range ATGWs on enemy tanks. Rarden is effective out to about 1500 metres. You may also have some Spartan vehicles fitted with the MCR in your vicinity. This system has exactly the same capability as ground-fired Milan but provides a measure of protection for the crew.

Tank support

When you operate in a mechanised battlegroup you will be supported by tanks. The tank is the most effective tank-killer of all. It can fire its armour-piercing discarding sabot (APDS) round out to 2000 metres with great

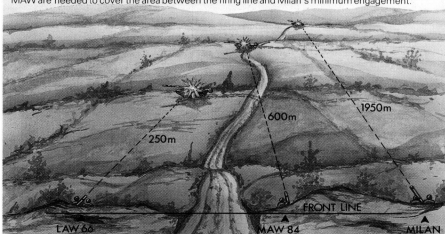

BRITISH ARMY INFANTRY ANTI-TANK WEAPONS RANGES

This is the coverage of weapons you will use in an infantry battalion. The 66-mm LAW and 84-mm MAW are needed to cover the area between the firing line and Milan's minimum engagement.

250 m

600 m

1950 m

LAW 66

MAW 84

FRONT LINE

MILAN

1. LAW can shoot out to 250 m.
2. MAW sight range is 600 m, but effective range is 500 m for static and 400 m for moving targets.
3. Milan can shoot out to 1950 m. Missile flight time is 12.5 seconds; you must be able to track the target for the whole time.

Above: The 66-mm LAW (Light Anti-tank Weapon) is a one-shot, recoilless, throwaway weapon, not particularly accurate and not capable of defeating modern MBT armour, though it has its uses for APCs and bunkers.

Below: Indirect artillery fire will not generally knock out Main Battle Tanks; however, it will cause them to 'close down', restricting their field of view, and fragments will smash optics and radio aerials and damage tracks and running gear.

Above: A light tank like the Scimitar is not designed to fight but to recce; the 30-mm Rarden cannon could damage a T-72 but certainly not knock it out. However, it would be very useful on BMPs and other APCs and thin-skinned vehicles.

accuracy, and at a rate of up to eight rounds a minute.

However, tanks are best used to achieve surprise. You will find that the Royal Armoured Corps no longer use tanks as static gun platforms. That would be a waste of their mobility. Keep them in reserve, ready to cut off and destroy any enemy tank penetration. You are equipped with Milan and perfectly capable of defending your position against tank attack without wasting your own tanks in static defence.

Armoured Reconnaissance Regiments are equipped with the Scorpion recce vehicle and with Striker. The highly accurate Swingfire ATGW is mounted on Striker and gives the Armoured Reconnaissance Regiment the ability to engage tanks out to a range of 4000 metres. This allows reconnaissance troops to cause early attrition.

Mines and choppers

The next component of your anti-tank plan is the minefield. This is a subject in itself; at this stage all you need to know is that the anti-tank mine plays an important part in the overall plan to defeat an enemy armoured attack.

There are several categories of anti-tank mine: the most common are the conventional cylindrical pressure mine (such as the British Mk 7), the bar mine, the off-route mine (designed to attack the side of a tank) and the scatterable mine which can be fired from a gun or launched from a system

mounted on an APC. Well-planned minefields covered by fire from your defensive positions can cause havoc among an enemy armoured formation.

Anti-tank helicopters are also a subject in themselves. TOW missiles fired from Lynx have a range out to 3750 metres. They are likely to engage massed enemy tank attacks of over 60 armoured vehicles well out to the front of you. Your role will be to mop up what is left.

A fighting chance

Add to this array of weapon systems the anti-tank capabilities of both artillery and offensive air support, and you will see that you stand a very good chance of blunting, stopping and destroying even the most concerted armoured threat. The tank is still a potent weapon system but it is no longer queen of the battlefield: the armoured helicopter is emerging as a contender for that title.

US ARMY INFANTRY ANTI-TANK WEAPONS RANGES

This shows the corresponding coverage for the US Army. TOW gives an extra kilometre over Milan, but there are not that many positions that will allow a clear shoot out to that range. Dragon again has better maximum range than MAW, but cannot be fired as rapidly.

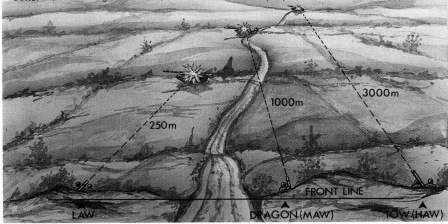

1. LAW: a more realistic range for engaging a tank would be 150 m or less, and volley fire is recommended.
2. Dragon can shoot out to 1000 m, and has a minimum range of 65 m. This gap is covered by LAW.
3. TOW can shoot out to 3000 m and must be carefully sighted to take advantage of this.

Combat Report
Oman:
SAS and Iranians Against the Adoo

In 1973 Robert Playfair was with BATT (British Army Training Team) on a four-month trip to Oman to help the Sultan against rebels. In one of the operations, an Iranian platoon operated with them.

We arrived in Salagh at our base camp and stayed there for about five days. During that time we were brought up to date on guerrilla movement in the Jabals. At the end of the briefing, we were to move up into the area.

We checked all our weapons and tested them on the old Firquat range, and were ready to move on Saturday morning. When we disembarked from the helicopter we were met by the head man of the loyal Firquat tribesmen and the Iranians' platoon commander at a location called Ravens Roost.

The first thing we had to do was to build our sangers and sleeping areas, which we did, using about 3,000 sandbags. Then we had to try to win the hearts and minds of the neighbouring villages.

We did this by having them come to us for medical treatment. We wanted them either to turn against the guerrillas or to isolate them, and it proved a very effective method of getting ideas of the enemy movements.

Next we started to get the Iranians working alongside us. We split into two teams – I took one and Jimmy the other – and we worked together for about two weeks to see how they operated. Their equipment was American and their uniform was not what we would call 'good desert camouflage' as it was too light in colour.

We started our march

Then, one day, there was some guerrilla movement in the Wadi Darbat, so we decided to try and catch them out. We had a very quick brief on how many men we would need to carry out the operation.

We were told that a platoon of Iranians would be going with us; we also had about 20 Firquats. When it was dark, we started our march towards the wadi. My boss Matt navigated for the first leg. I took over for the second leg, and Jimmy did the third. We arrived at Wadi Darbat at about 0200 hours and immediately started to make our defence sangers.

The next morning, small arms fire started coming on to our position. I was behind the machine-gun and we pinpointed the source of some of the fire. The Iranians were nearly all down in their sangers; however, their weapons were out on top, and they were firing away at goodness knows what.

The small-arms fire came in for most of that day. They started to use it as air bursts, but there were no casualties. They then started to mortar us, but most of the rounds were dropping short, apart from four or so that landed on the position. As it began to get dark everything just stopped.

The sky lit up

Then the Iranian platoon commander came over to my boss and said that he was taking his platoon down into the wadi. I looked at Matt and he looked at me, and he said to the Iranian, "Are you kidding?". But he wasn't. We tried to tell him that it would be suicide even to try to go into that wadi at night and that they would have sleepers out, but he wouldn't take 'No' for an answer.

Even after the Firquat leader said it all again in Arabic, he still wanted to go ahead. He called the platoon and had a short word with them, and the next thing we saw was the Iranians going off in single file.

We could still see them about 600 metres away as their American uniforms were so light. If we could see them, the Adoo guerrillas would have an even easier job.

The next thing we had to do was to reorganise the defence of the position as we were now about 24 men less than a platoon. But we knew that the Adoo would never attack at night, apart from firing some small arms fire from the far side of the wadi.

By now the Iranians had been gone for about 40 minutes, and we couldn't hear anything. We said to each other that everything must be all right, but no sooner had the words left our lips than we heard a lot of small arms fire and knew that the Iranians had walked into a sleeper. The sky lit up with tracer bullets and there was very heavy firing.

After about 20 minutes the firing suddenly stopped, and the radio operator said that the Iranians were asking for BATT's help. I turned to

The Firquats were counter-guerrillas trained and led by SAS teams. Many had only recently changed sides and commanding them was delicate.

Matt and said that I hoped he didn't think I was going down there, and he just laughed and said, 'No'. Although I have had some hairy moments, I was in no hurry to die. But we knew that we would have to help them, so we waited until first light.

I took my BATT team plus six Firquats with me, and we moved off down the slope of the wadi, using the thick bush as cover. We contoured along the left-hand side, expecting to be bumped by the Adoo but not making any contact at all. When we were about 200 metres from the Iranians we stopped and got down, and I used the radio to make contact with them.

The last thing I wanted was for them to open up on us, so I told them that I was moving in from the south side of the wadi and gave them our position. When we finally got to them we found that they had received casualties, including two dead.

If only he had listened

I called up Matt and explained the situation to him. I told him that we were going to carry out the dead and casualties, as it was far too dangerous to bring in a helicopter; the Adoo could be waiting for us to do just that and would then strike with AK-47s and RPG-7s.

We started the long haul back to our position, and when we arrived we quickly got the wounded behind sangers, in case we were hit again. By this time, my boss had got through to Salagh and had called in an air strike to rake the wadi north of our position and requested a helicopter.

The aircraft used rockets and cannon fire, and the helicopter arrived to take away the wounded and dead. When this was over we packed up and moved on to do a follow-up operation.

As for the young Iranian commander, he just didn't know what to do. He had lost men who should never have been lost. If only he had listened to us; we had been there so many times, and knew that the Adoo were very clever enemies. When they saw the Iranians moving around in the wadi at night they would have known that they were on to a very good shoot.

The follow-up ended with no more contact with the Adoo, so we moved back across the desert to our home base of Ravens Roost. I for one was glad to get it over with, and said to myself, "When is this bloody war going to end?"

The Sultan of Oman's troops, seen here on the back of a Land Rover. They were assisted by large numbers of American-trained Iranian soldiers who had been sent by the Shah.

TANK HUNTING

Snarling, heavily-armoured, and bristling with devastating armament, the main battle tank can seem unstoppable to the infantryman — but there are occasions when determined and properly armed foot-soldiers can wreak havoc among even a sizeable detachment of enemy armour.

You'll usually carry out such operations at night, as part of a fighting patrol whose mission is to destroy enemy tanks at close range.

Known as tank hunting, this is a task for the ordinary infantryman, as distinct from the expert and highly specialised techniques of anti-tank warfare. This section of the Combat Skills course details the weapons and techniques of tank hunting and tells you the vulnerable parts of an armoured vehicle that you should aim to hit.

Know the weak spots

The first thing you need to remember is that a tank is not by any means a flexible weapon. Closed down for combat, a tank crew has very limited vision. Close to, a tank is surrounded by blind spots.

TANK VULNERABILITY

1. Tanks have restricted vision when all their hatches are closed.
2. Soviet tanks in particular cannot depress their main armament very far, and are especially vulnerable when crossing a ridge.
3. The sides, rear and belly of a tank have much thinner armour than the front, which is usually proof against infantry anti-tank weapons.
4. Tanks are particularly vulnerable when re-fuelling and re-arming: they are stationary and bunched up.
5. Despite developments in thermal imagers, it is still difficult for a tank crew to spot infantry at night, especially if they use correct camouflage and concealment.
5. Tanks without infantry support are particularly vulnerable to infantry anti-tank weapons, especially in woods or built-up areas.

A Soviet BMP Infantry Fighting Vehicle leads a mixed column of tanks and infantry. Successful tank hunting demands a thorough knowledge of the strengths and weaknesses of enemy armoured vehicles.

The tank's armament is virtually useless against a moving, close-range target, for the simple reason that it can't lower its gun sufficiently to engage a nearby target. As a result, a tank is at its most vulnerable when crossing a ridge — doubly so, in fact, because its tracks and lightly-armoured belly, rear and sides are also exposed then.

Tanks have to refuel and rearm, usually at night. They'll do this either in a 'leaguer' (an administrative compound) or with a 'running replenishment' in the field. In either case enemy tanks will be bunched together, with little room to manoeuvre, and probably surrounded by cover that may screen them but also offers a perfect hiding-place for infantry. If you can find the enemy's tanks at such a time, they make excellent targets.

Attack by patrol

Imagine that you have been given the task of mounting a tank-hunting patrol. Your mission is to destroy as many tanks as possible as they undergo running replenishment in a

Taking aim with a Carl Gustav 84-mm recoilless rifle: this bulky but accurate weapon will penetrate the side and rear armour of modern Soviet tanks as long as they do not carry reactive armour panels.

village street just behind enemy lines. You know that the enemy has been using that location for two nights and that his tanks will be there again tonight. Recce patrols have already found a route for you between two forward enemy companies. You're to take a 12-man patrol.

As with any patrol, your first job is to make sure you know as much as possible about the killing ground and your route to it. Use maps, aerial photographs, and if possible survey the ground itself from an observation post.

Next, learn everything you can about the type of tank you are going to attack: where its most vulnerable points are, its hatches, radio antennae, and sights. And make yourself fami-

liar with enemy operating procedures.

Finally, rehearse your action on the objective and make sure that you and everyone going with you knows exactly what they have to do.

The weapons to take

Since your best chance of success lies in reaching your objective, making a quick attack and then withdrawing behind your own lines as fast and as unobtrusively as possible, you would ideally use timed charges. However, they are likely to be reserved for Special Forces.

A reasonable armoury of immediate-effect weapons for your 12-man patrol would include two 84-mm medium anti-tank weapons (MAWs), two 66-mm light anti-tank weapons

TANK HUNTING

Tank hunting is carried out by a fighting patrol which can vary in size from a section to several companies. The fighting patrol must have sufficient strength to carry out the mission and defend itself on route out and route back. The basic aim is to attack enemy tanks when they are harboured up, in a defensive position or in a tank leaguer.

Control, concealment and protection
As soon as you start firing your anti-tank weapons your position will be revealed to the enemy, so make sure you deploy these weapons at reasonable intervals, not all together.

Co-ordinate your fire
Make sure you can cover targets with both small-arms and anti-tank fire. A good co-ordinated fire plan will isolate individual tanks from their infantry support, restrict tank crews vision by forcing them to close down, and cut off the unit you are attacking from enemy reinforcements.

Withdrawal route
Make sure you have a secure withdrawal route, and leave a protection party back at the final RV. Everyone must know the signal for 'Break Contact' and what he must do. Withdrawal must be staggered, so that the enemy will not be keen to follow you up. Leapfrog back by half sections so that the enemy is always under fire while you withdraw.

Surprise
Your chances of success depend on catching the enemy unawares: your presence should be announced by a sudden hail of anti-tank and small arms fire. Your patrolling skills and fieldcraft will have to be excellent.

Information
Tank hunting relies on good intelligence information received in time to allow for careful planning and detailed preparation. Every eventuality must be covered.

Other weapons
Don't forget white phosphorus grenades: these are particularly effective against dismounted tank crew and add to the confusion. These grenades are also useful to cover your withdrawal, since they produce instant smoke and discourage the enemy from putting his head up.

Mines
Don't just use the 66-mm and 84-mm anti-tank weapons; plant anti-tank mines on likely enemy routes and approaches. Always mix some anti-personnel mines with the anti-tank mines to discourage the enemy engineers from digging them up.

ZSU 23-4
Remember, these self-propelled anti-aircraft guns can be used against ground targets with devastating effect. Get rid of them first! Even small-arms fire will wreck their optics and radar control system.

The 84-mm is a sizeable beast, but it needs to be in order to fire a large enough round to threaten a Main Battle Tank. In recent years tanks have received new types of armour designed to defeat infantry anti-tank weapons.

Timed charges and Molotov cocktails
Make sure these have been properly prepared before the patrol. Satchel charges should be double-fused to ensure that they detonate.

Know your enemy
You must be completely familiar with enemy AFVs and their tactics. You have to know what you are firing at.

(LAWs), both firing specialised high-explosive anti-tank (HEAT) missiles. The LAW is effective up to 200 metres, the MAW out to twice that distance. Both will penetrate the sides and rear of any Soviet main battle tank.

In addition you'll be carrying phosphorus grenades, anti-tank mines and personal weapons.

You can attach image intensification (II) equipment or an individual weapon sight (IWS) to the MAW. This will give you an impressive picture of any nocturnal enemy activity at up to 150 yards' range even on the darkest night. Without an IWS, you will need white light – flares – to score a kill at anything but point-blank range.

USING DEAD SPACE

All tanks have restricted vision, especially when the hatches are closed and the crew are entirely reliant on observation equipment to spot enemy infantry. You can exploit this weakness by firing rifles and machine-guns at a tank to force the crew to close down. Also, the main armament of a tank cannot be depressed to hit a target within about 20 metres. By taking advantage of dead space you can approach and destroy even the latest enemy tank.

20 metres dead space of principal weapons

10 metres visual dead space:

principal direction of fire and observation when turret is pointing forward

tank crew cannot see you

most favourable direction of attack when turret forward

20 metre main gun dead space

10 metre visual dead space from gunner's station

The main armament cannot hit you if you are within 20 metres and no-one can see you if you are within 10 metres.

ARMOUR THICKNESS

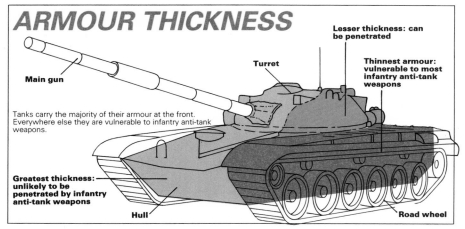

Main gun

Turret

Lesser thickness: can be penetrated

Thinnest armour: vulnerable to most infantry anti-tank weapons

Tanks carry the majority of their armour at the front. Everywhere else they are vulnerable to infantry anti-tank weapons.

Greatest thickness: unlikely to be penetrated by infantry anti-tank weapons

Hull

Road wheel

LAW 80 is supposed to enter service with the British Army in 1987, and will substantially improve the infantry's anti-tank capability. It is a one-shot, throwaway weapon like the 66-mm, but with a much more effective warhead.

You cock the 66-mm by pulling the top handle forward. There is a cartoon 'idiot's guide' printed on the side, but it is not recommended that you read through this in sight of a hostile tank!

Into the attack

You should open fire with both MAWs and LAWs simultaneously. This creates the maximum immediate damage to the target and creates an invaluable psychological advantage.

Imagine the effect on the enemy: he thinks he is in a safe administrative area, behind his own lines, peaceably servicing his tanks. Then, several HEAT missiles slam into the vehicles.

Flames and panic break out everywhere. The tanks are waiting in column to be refuelled. Some reverse, others accelerate, some swerve to avoid other crippled and burning vehicles. At this point you should drop anti-tank mines at each end of the column, causing further damage and chaos. Meanwhile, rake any visible enemy personnel with automatic fire.

About now some enemy crews will decide to abandon their ruined vehicles. At this stage, throw as many phosphorus grenades as you can into the midst of the tanks. This will disrupt any night vision equipment the enemy is trying to bring to bear on your position, and injure dismounting

AIMING POINTS AGAINST WARSAW PACT AFVs

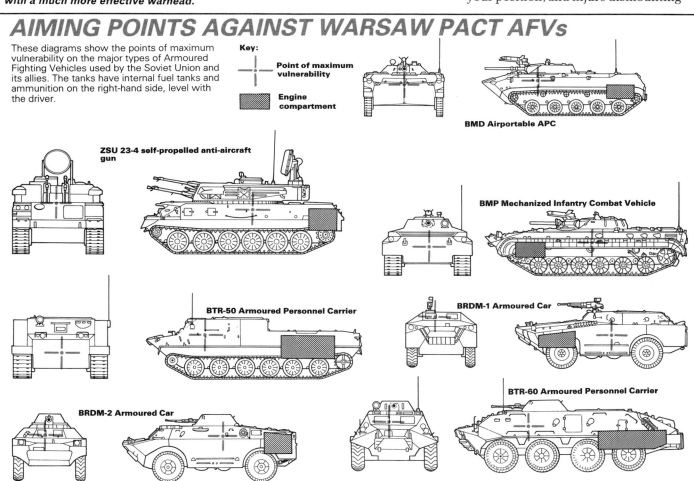

These diagrams show the points of maximum vulnerability on the major types of Armoured Fighting Vehicles used by the Soviet Union and its allies. The tanks have internal fuel tanks and ammunition on the right-hand side, level with the driver.

Key:

⊕ **Point of maximum vulnerability**

▨ **Engine compartment**

BMD Airportable APC

ZSU 23-4 self-propelled anti-aircraft gun

BMP Mechanized Infantry Combat Vehicle

BTR-50 Armoured Personnel Carrier

BRDM-1 Armoured Car

BTR-60 Armoured Personnel Carrier

BRDM-2 Armoured Car

In the prone position an 84-mm team is very difficult to spot from a closed-down tank. A reverse slope is a doubly good position, because the tank presents its vulnerable belly.

enemy troops. Having done your job, withdraw as discreetly as you can.

The ambush option

You can bring off an attack as successful as that only against an extremely inefficient enemy. But that is the ideal to aim for. In practice, most of your tank hunting will more nearly resemble an ambush.

If, for instance, you were withdrawing under the pressure of an enemy attack, one way of blunting his advance would be to set up tank ambushes and hit the enemy as he advanced. You'll be able to mount these attacks most easily in close country or in built-up areas. If you can mount a series of ambushes, so much the better.

Choose your ambush site carefully. From it you should be able to get as close as between 100 and 200 yards to the enemy. Spring your ambush, withdraw along a pre-planned route,

reorganise and repeat the process.

Any decently-trained tank crew will, if they can, avoid areas where they're vulnerable to ambush. And if they're forced to advance through close or built-up areas, they'll call on infantry to clear the woods or buildings first. However, in reality, tanks often outrun their infantry support – if

they can get it at all. You will usually find rich pickings in a tank-hunting party working from a well-chosen ambush site.

Where to aim

The largest 'soft' area of a tank you're likely to see is its side. So wait until your target tank turns away from you before opening fire.

Tank tracks are particularly vulnerable. If you can blow off a track, the tank is as good as dead. It's immediately exposed as an easy kill for longer-range anti-tank missiles, and is costly for the enemy to recover.

The turret or the glacis plate at the front of the tank is where a tank's armour is hardest. Don't fire at the front of a tank, therefore, even if it's coming straight at you. Just take cover.

An infantryman hidden behind a building, an earth bank or in his trench is surprisingly safe from a tank. If one motors over your trench, just keep your head down. Then pop up behind it and send a LAW or MAW up its rear end.

Revenge is sweet

Tank hunting is a useful way for the infantryman to get back at the tank. It's not a practical way to destroy enemy armour in large numbers: this is a job for other tanks, long-range anti-tank missiles and anti-tank guided missiles (ATGW) on the open battle-field.

But tank-hunting saps the enemy's morale and raises that of the foot-soldier no end – as well as reducing the threat to you from enemy armour. Tank hunting is the infantry's special contribution to the anti-tank battle.

When it's successful, tank hunting is truly an example of David slaying Goliath.

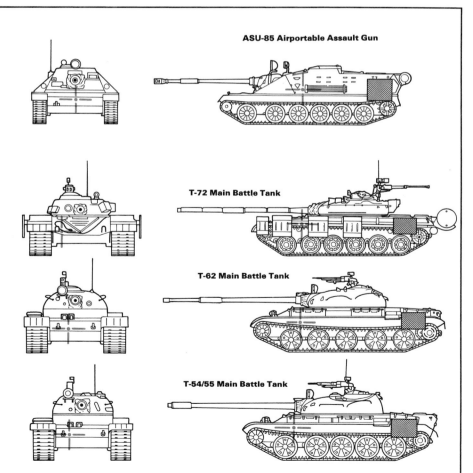

ASU-85 Airportable Assault Gun

T-72 Main Battle Tank

T-62 Main Battle Tank

T-54/55 Main Battle Tank

Combat Report
Malaysia:
'Hearts and Minds' Part 1

A former member of the SAS Regiment describes his experiences in Malaysia with a small team of troops sent to win the 'hearts and minds' of the villagers along the border with Borneo and Indonesia. Many of the tribesmen had never seen a white man before, and winning them over presented novel problems to the British soldiers.

When the confrontation between Indonesia and the fledgling Malaysia ended in 1968, the British presence was reduced to a mere token force, as the terrorist problem officially no longer existed.

In practice, however, there was still a problem, and the best military solution lay in wholesale search-and-destroy missions. But the British could not overtly engage in such operations, and so they were disguised as 'hearts and minds' operations.

There were, and still are, many primitive tribes living in the highlands. They were officially designated as being Aboriginal Peoples; government policy was to try to educate them slowly into the ways of civilisation, restricting contact to essential medical services.

It was my job to speak

So it was that various elements of Far East Land Forces found themselves ostensibly visiting Aborigine villagers (when they could find them) in order to dispense medical supplies and basic medical aid. Weapons and ammunition could be carried because these were always taken into the jungle, even on exercise.

I was attached to a 'hearts and minds' team as a specialist in combat intelligence. It was my job to talk — usually via an interpreter — to the headman of any village we came to and find out if there was any activity in the area. Gradually, I'd hope to build up some sort of picture of any terrorist organisation, figuring out who they were, where they were based, what weapons they had and so on.

As well as myself, we had a signaller, a medic, four minders who could act independently if they had to, an interpreter/tracker who spoke some of the local dialects,

and the boss, a young captain who came from the same regiment as the minders.

All in all, it was one of the best jobs I ever had — we were on our own and I got to see the kinds of people that you only ever read about: the Aborigines. Lovely, gentle people they were, but a little confused by all the attention they were suddenly getting — and a little confused by some of the medical practices they were being taught.

I remember one village we came to, the headman came out to meet us and the old boy had a very well-developed chest — a sort of geriatric Page Three. It worried our medic quite a bit until finally we found out what had happened. Apparently a government team had been there about a year before, preaching the virtues of birth control. Then, when they left, they gave the village a year's supply of birth control pills. Well, there was no way that the headman was going to let valuable medicine be used by mere women, so he scoffed the lot himself. And, as a result, he developed breasts, as well as beginning to talk in a high-pitched voice. Our medic explained that an enemy had cursed the medicine and with great ceremony the remaining pills were burnt.

We used to travel initially by Land Rover or canoe, though sometimes we were choppered in. We'd choose one village as a base and then try to cover a 10 to 20 mile radius around it. For weapons we had Armalites, SLRs, shotguns, grenades, some Claymore mines and a GPMG. Usually, the boss and a couple of minders would disappear off on their own for two or three days, particularly if we got what looked like hard info on a terrorist group somewhere in the area.

I was driving the Land Rover

In theory, if we found that there was a terrorist group nearby we were supposed to contact HQ Farelf, who would contact the Malaysian authorities, who would send in their own boys. In practice, if the boss thought that we couldn't handle it ourselves, he'd get in touch with another 'hearts and minds' team who would whistle over to give a hand.

I'm not sure, but I think that prisoners were regarded as being an embarrassment so, if there was any action, terrorists who weren't killed were allowed to get away — after all, the more stories they told their mates in Thailand or Burma about how unfriendly Malaya had suddenly become, the better for all of us.

The first time I saw action, I was driving the Land Rover back from the nearest town some 30 klicks away. The track was an old logging road, so it was quite wide though the ruts were brutal. There was tall, primary jungle on one side and burnt-out lallang (secondary jungle) on the other.

"Sorry, Johnny!"

Anyway, suddenly I heard that sharp 'pop-pop-pop' that means some joker's using an SMG, and the front offside tyre was blown out. This was at the very start of the 'hearts and minds' campaign so I don't think the terrorists had realised that the Brits posed an actual threat. But in a mad moment I got out of the vehicle — which, anyway, had slewed across the track — and shouted out: "You effing idiot, I'm British!" Funny what goes through your mind at the time . . . all I can remember now is being furious because I'd have to spend time repairing the bloody tyre!

There was a moment of silence during which I suddenly realised that I was not in a good position and that maybe I should try to sneak off into the lallang behind me. Then I heard a voice from the primary jungle shouting, "Sorry, Johnny!" Then, nothing. After about half an hour I finished shaking, changed the tyre — have you ever tried changing a tyre from underneath a vehicle? — and got back to camp. The boss and the minders were still laughing about it weeks later, and for a time it looked as if 'British Johnny' was going to be my permanent nickname!

If we had terrorist contact while on patrol we were supposed to radio for Malaysian troops to deal with them, but in practice if we needed help we contacted the nearest British unit.

Combat Skills
AMBUSHING TANKS

Afghan guerrillas pose for the camera on the wreck of a Soviet *BMP* that they ambushed. Hit by an *RPG*-7 anti-tank rocket, the *BMP* brewed up, taking most of its crew with it. Visibility from most armoured vehicles is poor, and in forested or built-up areas the infantryman can successfully ambush the most powerful Main Battle Tank.

It is easy to think of anti-tank helicopters or other tanks as the main anti-tank weapon systems on the battlefield. This is only half right. The other tank killer is you: the infantryman, armed with a variety of portable anti-tank weapon systems. Even though some of these systems, particularly MILAN, allow you to stand off from your target and engage at ranges of up to 2,000 metres, most of the systems require you to be much closer. And one way of getting close to your target is to ambush it.

Normally a force of platoon strength will be given the task of carrying out a tank ambush. Before you embark on your patrol to the ambush site you must prepare your operation carefully and precisely. Make sure that you have all the information that you will need to ensure a successful ambush, especially a genuine knowledge of enemy tank tactics, capabilities and techniques.

The Soviet BMP's armour is thin: this is the exit hole left by the copper slug in the RPG-7 round that penetrated the side armour, passed through the interior and out the other side.

Choose the most appropriate method of attack for the planned target and the terrain. In Germany you are most likely to carry out a tank ambush in wooded or close country or in or from a built-up area. Germany is becoming increasingly urbanised and is already heavily wooded; enemy tanks are therefore naturally channelled between these obstacles. Woods and villages may often be less than a kilometre apart, so if you fire from the wood or village edge most of your targets are likely to be less than 500 metres away.

Anti-tank weapons

In addition to your platoon medium anti-tank weapons or MAWs (currently the 84-mm Carl Gustav) and your light anti-tank weapon or LAWs (currently the disposable 66-mm) — both soon to be replaced by LAW 80 — you may decide to take anti-tank mines, Claymore mines, phosphorus grenades, cratering charges or 'Molotov' cocktails. In Germany the enemy formation you are likely to ambush will include motor rifle troops in APCs as well as tanks. In other theatres the column may include lorried infantry, towed artillery or logistic vehicles.

You will have a choice of mines. Current British mines are the Mk 7 anti-tank mine, the L3AI anti-tank mine (non-metallic), the L9AI bar mine and the off-route L14AI anti-tank mine.

Using anti-tank mines

The Mk 7 mine is a heavy metal mine containing 9 kg of explosive with an all-up weight of 14.5 kg. You can't carry too many of these for a long distance! However, it will cut the track of the heaviest-known tank and can be fitted with a booby trap. The mine is fired by the No. 5 Double Impulse Fuse, which will defeat tanks fitted with mine rollers; it will not operate under the weight of a man.

The Light L3AI non-metallic mine contains 6 kg of explosive and weighs 8 kg. If you remove the metal detector ring the mine is not detectable (unlike the Mk7) by electronic detectors. The

Tactical use of the 66-mm LAW

The 66-mm Light Anti-Tank Weapon (LAW) is not capable of knocking out the latest generation of Soviet Main Battle Tanks or of dealing with a vehicle equipped with reactive armour. The British Army is replacing the LAW with LAW 80, a more accurate and more powerful weapon, but until this has been adopted you have to do the best you can with the 66-mm.

It is perhaps most useful for 'bunker busting'. It has, in addition to a point contact fuse, a 'graze' fuse so that the round will detonate even without striking a target squarely. Even if you don't hit anything, the shock effect of the round bursting is considerable, and should give you the vital few seconds to get the enemy before he recovers enough to return fire.

A well-aimed shot from a 66-mm LAW can still achieve a 'mobility kill' against a tank by wrecking its tracks. LAW is also perfectly capable of taking out lightly-armoured vehicles like Soviet APCs.

TANK AMBUSHING

The British Army of the Rhine is deployed in an area dotted with large forestry blocks, towns and villages. You can force the enemy to deploy by engaging his armour in the open ground with long-range anti-tank systems sited in the woods and villages; in this close country you can do real damage with infantry anti-tank weapons, mines and demolition charges. Use obstacles and mines to channel the enemy into selecting lines of advance on which you have positioned your ambushes. Here you can hit the enemy hard on your own terms, withdraw, and hit him again. To do this successfully your tank ambush drills have to be slick.

Ambush positions
These should be manned by at least a section, and the 84 MAW and 66 LAW should be sited where they can fire into the side of the enemy tanks and be protected by Claymores and GPMG fire from infantry assault.

Protection
If you have time to dig in, do so, as this will protect you from return fire; and overhead cover is vital in woods if the enemy calls in artillery.

Siting
Choose an ambush position where the trees are close enough together to prevent movement by armour off the track you are ambushing.

Assess enemy strength
If their armour is supported by large quantities of infantry or if they get a chance to dismount in force from their BMPs, you could be in real trouble: set up the ambush so that the enemy can drive through. Here the advantages of command-detonated mines are obvious.

A sheep flees to cover as a 21-mm sub-calibre training round goes wide of the target on a firing range in Wales. Even against a static target, not firing back at 150 metres, it is not easy to achieve a hit with LAW.

The same target is hit with a live 66-mm round from a LAW: although its armour penetration is no longer sufficient to destroy the latest tanks, the warhead still has its uses.

The answer to a modern tank: volley-fired 66-mm LAWS. If you each prepare two and fire a couple of synchornised volleys, the tank should be hit several times, hopefully forcing the crew to bail out.

Springing the ambush
To avoid early detection, create the road block as the ambush is sprung by destroying the lead vehicle by anti-tank fire or mines, or by using an explosive device placed in a culvert. You should destroy the rear vehicle at the same time.

Night action
Trip flares are very good if carefully sited; they can also be electrically detonated and used in clusters. Schermuly flares tend to give away the firer's position, and their use must be carefully co-ordinated with fire from the anti-armour weapons. Mortar and artillery illumination illuminate too great an area and can only be used in large-scale ambushes.

White phosphorus grenades
Excellent for creating a bit of mayhem. They also degrade night vision equipment and burn dismounting crews. This use of smoke is particularly useful, as motor rifle troops in BMPs are likely to be encountered.

Timed charges and Molotov cocktails
Prepare these well in advance.

Off-route mine
This is totally devastating against vehicles and effective against all WarPac main battle tanks. It can be initiated either by the target breaking a collapsing circuit or by means of a command wire.

Observation posts
These should be sited well forward to give advance warning of enemy approach, their strength and their direction of movement.

Road blocks
These can be created by felling suitable large trees or blowing craters. If they are not covered by fire, they should be mined and booby-trapped. Do not forget to mark them on the friendly side to prevent 'own goals'.

Mines
Decide where you are going to knock out the lead vehicle, and mine the area around it so that the following vehicles cannot drive round it out of the ambush. The same applies to the last vehicle: preferably you should choose a killing zone where there is no room to turn round.

Libyan BMPs lie abandoned in the Sahara desert after an ambush by troops loyal to President Habre of Chad. The area is being bombed by Libyan aircraft trying to destroy vehicles and equipment captured by Chadian forces. Moral: don't hang about at the site of an ambush.

L3AI is only available in limited numbers and so is unlikely to be used for large defensive minefields, which makes it particularly suitable for laying by hand singly or in small numbers in a tank ambush. It will cut the track of the heaviest known tank.

The L9AI bar mine weighs 10.5 kg and contains 8.5 kg of explosive. It is designed to produce the same effect as a cylindrical mine while using a lower density of mines (it is 1.2 m long and 0.1 m wide). It too will cut the track of the heaviest known tank.

Off-route mine

It is, though, the L14AI off-route anti-tank mine that is especially suitable for tank ambush; it can be set up quickly and covers a wide frontage. As its name implies, it is designed for use to one side of a track.

It is usually set to fire horizontally at the passing target vehicle, and is set off when the vehicle ruptures the breakwire which is laid in its path. It is designed to penetrate up to 70 mm of armour and has a maximum range of 80 metres, but it is at its most effective up to 40 metres. Its minimum range is two metres.

You can also site the mine to fire upwards, for example through a street manhole, to attack the belly of a tank; or downwards, for example from a window, to attack the top. The explosive is generally more effective against the top or belly of a tank than against its side, where road wheels and other appendages can reduce its effectiveness.

You will usually lay the mine so that it is set off by the target vehicle, but you can also set it up for command detonation, for instance by breaking the wire yourself at the required moment.

It will take you and only two other members of your patrol between five and 20 minutes, depending upon your skill and the nature of the site, to set up an off-route mine.

Value of grenades

You should also take phosphorus grenades and Claymore mines. The grenades will create confusion, degrade enemy night vision devices and cause burn injuries to dismounting crews. Site Claymore mines to kill dismounting troops and to protect the flanks of your ambush position against counter or surprise attack.

Having selected your mix of weapons, you now choose a suitable position for your ambush, from your personal knowledge of the battlefield, as a result of air reconnaissance, or just from having studied the ground on a map. Choose a defile or where the road passes between woods, large ditches, thick hedges, banks or buildings. If your ambush is slightly longer range and is crossing the open ground between two villages or woods, make

WHITE LIGHT

The **Schermuly flare** (top left); the **pencil signal flare** (top right); and a **trip flare** (bottom). The Schermuly is a parachute flare that can give the enemy time to take cover as it flies up into the air. The trip flare provides instant white light at ground level, but must be carefully sited so that it illuminates the enemy, not the ambushers. Screens and mirrors can be used to increase its effect.

sure that your wood frontage or village edge is defendable.

Springing the ambush

When the enemy tanks and APCs enter your ambush, attempt to disable the leading and rear vehicles. Site your MAWs and LAWs to engage targets from a flank. As your anti-tank projectiles slam into the sides of the enemy tanks, all hell will break loose. Some tanks will 'brew up', others will be immobilised, and some crews will attempt to leave their burning vehicles. Use your LSWs and Claymore mines to engage these crewmen and the supporting infantry who will debus in order to counter-attack your position.

In close country it is not the tanks

THE OFF-ROUTE MINE

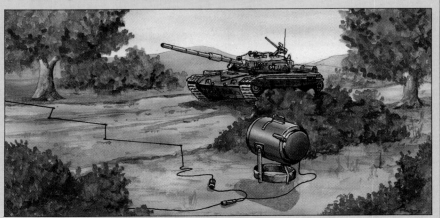

This has a shaped-charge warhead, detonated when a tank runs over the wire stretched across the road. It will penetrate the side armour of any current tank, but if the copper slug hits the tank's wheels the tank may be immobilised rather than completely destroyed. You can position the mine in a tree or building, angled to fire against the vulnerable top armour of an enemy tank.

A SECTION VEHICLE AMBUSH

enemy approach

road

Site your vehicle ambush where the enemy will be trapped on the road, unable to turn round or drive away across country. Use defiles where the road passes between obstacles such as thick hedges, woods or high banks.

Whether or not you crater the road, your first anti-tank rounds should be used to destroy the leading vehicle and, if possible, the rear vehicle. This blocks the enemy in the ambush area and gives you the best possible target.

Claymore mines

Claymore detonation control lines

bridge

stream

crater

Section main body (should include 2 LAW and 1 MAW)

ambush area

Claymore mines

crater (to be blown once the enemy are in the ambush area)

GPMG team (able to fire down the road)

As with an infantry ambush, make sure the signal for opening fire is known by everyone in the ambush party and that the withdrawal route is equally clear.

A Soviet BRDM armoured car from a reconnaissance unit knocked out by Afghan guerrillas. It brewed up after being hit: another victim of a successful vehicle ambush.

that will be the greatest threat to you, especially if you have prepared your ambush positions well by digging in: it is the enemy infantry who can get in amongst you who are the real threat. If you have chosen slightly rising ground and have the time to sow anti-personnel mines in front of your positions, you will be able to hold off a numerically larger enemy force for a surprisingly long time, long enough certainly to cause untold damage to his armoured vehicles. Relatively small numbers of Viet Cong ambushed US armoured columns in Vietnam with great success and then, at the right moment, vanished into the jungle.

Safe withdrawal

The timing of your withdrawal is likely to be crucial to the success of your operation. However many enemy tanks you destroy, your patrol will only be successful if you manage to extricate yourselves safely and with the minimum of casualties. You should therefore withdraw when the enemy is still surprised and shocked by your ambush, and before he starts to recover and reorganise.

The tank ambush is a classic infantry tactic. It relies upon stealth, cunning, surprise and shock action. It takes advantage of the main weaknesses of tanks. Above all, it provides the infantryman with the opportunity to meet strong enemy armoured columns on equal terms.

PRINCIPLES OF FITNESS

1 Frequency of training

Improvement in fitness is directly related to the frequency of your exercise. In the early stages, four or five training sessions a week will stimulate a significant improvement in your fitness level.

Once you have achieved this level of activity and reached your planned level of fitness, three sessions a week will probably be sufficient to maintain fitness. Less than two sessions per week is of limited value.

Included planned rest days so that repair of tissues and replenishment of energy (glycogen) can take place. Rest days will also provide essential physical and mental relaxation. It is all a question of balance.

2 Intensity of training

To improve fitness, your heart rate must be raised beyond its normal output, i.e. to between 70 and 85 per cent of its maximum capacity. This improvement is referred to as the 'training zone' and will be explained more fully later on in the course.

You should push yourself – but not too hard. Always remember the 'conversation test'; you should be just able to talk to a buddy while running etc.

3 Duration of training

In the initial stages you should aim to exercise for at least 20 minutes within your 'training zone'. As you get fitter, you will be able to increase the duration up to 45 minutes. However, 20 minutes will be quite sufficient for a relatively unfit person.

4 Type of activity

You should include aerobic ('with oxygen') activity together with muscle-strengthening and flexibility exercises. Aerobic activity (walking, jogging, cycling, swimming, rowing etc) is the best type of exercise as it improves cardiovascular fitness and involves large muscle groups.

As a soldier, you will have to yomp, carry kit, handle a weapon and drag a casualty to cover. You therefore need a good deal of upper body strength, and this type of exercise is vital.

There are many benefits of getting – and staying – fit, and the small amount of time you invest will be more than adequately repaid by the feeling of being fit.

The Fitness Test will establish your current level of fitness so that you can set yourself specific targets in a general time frame. Follow the specific principles of a good exercise programme.

Benefits of fitness

When you're fit, you will:

1 Have more energy
2 Have fewer health disorders
3 Improve your personal appearance
4 Feel good

1 More energy

A body that is physically fit has more energy available so that daily physical activity does not drain it of its resources. Not only can it perform more physical activity, but it can recover faster. It also has a larger 'energy reserve' to cope with sudden demands.

2 Fewer health disorders

A trained and physically fit body is less susceptible to cardiovascular disorders than an unfit one.

Less stress is placed upon the body and it works efficiently and economically. Good health is greatly enhanced by regular exercise and good nutrition – which should be a lifetime habit.

3 Improved personal appearance

Your health is the most precious thing you can ever have – no amount of money can buy it. When you get fit, everyone notices you because good health radiates from you. Low body fat, increased muscle tone and good posture are the rewards for regular exercise.

Starting out

It will help you enormously if you keep in mind some essential 'principles of success'.

1 Define your aim

In the military, targets are set; but otherwise you have to set your own. Decide on exactly the level of fitness that you wish to achieve. One of the reasons for drop-out is because of the lack of a well-defined plan.

2 Set definite targets

Write a clear, concise statement of your target and the time limit for its achievement. Make it realistic: fitness is a lifetime habit and it would be foolish to try to change the effects of a lifetime of neglect overnight. However, you will be amazed by the progress that you can achieve over a short period with a concentrated amount of effort.

3 Develop persistence

Most of us are good starters but poor finishers, prone to giving up at the first signs of defeat. We must gradually develop persistence to overcome temporary setbacks.

There is no substitute for persistence; we may lose the battle occasionally, but not the war. Remember: 'When the going gets tough, the tough get going'.

4 Total commitment

You must become totally committed to your aims and concentrate all your attention on achieving them. Learn how to commit yourself totally and without reservation.

5 Make time

Plan ahead and put down definite times for working out – don't leave it until it's 'convenient'.

6 Team spirit

You must avoid those who are less committed than yourself. Gather as many positive thinkers around you as possible for mutual support. In the early stages try to work out with a group, and later develop a 'buddy system' and work out with someone of similar ability.

7 Do it now

Putting things off leads to failure. The time will never be exactly right, so no matter what the circumstances do it now – even if you do not feel 'ready'.

8 Reward yourself

Nature will reward you for your efforts many times over in the long run, but in the short term give yourself some small rewards for targets achieved. Pleasure is a great motivator!

4 Feeling good

When you work out, you stimulate your whole body to peak efficiency, both mentally and physically. Fit people feel good about themselves and this gives them a lot of confidence. Remind yourself of these benefits whenever you work out.

Team spirit is vital: exercises requiring team effort and co-ordination help build you and your mates into a fighting unit rather than a collection of individuals.

Get the right kit

Investing in the right kit can help prevent injury and will improve your image. Under military training all kit is issued, but do not expect refinements. Most trained ranks invest in a good tracksuit (cotton to absorb sweat); good training shoes with shock-free soles; and a pair of comfortable shorts as well as a couple of T-shirts.

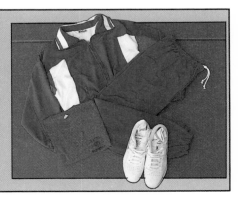

TYPES OF EXERCISE FOR TOTAL FITNESS

Before starting to get fit, you need to understand the different types of exercise and their place in a total fitness programme.

Cardiovascular (heart and lung) fitness will need to include elements of aerobic ('with oxygen') and **anaerobic** ('without oxygen') exercise. Muscle toning fitness needs elements of **isometric, isotonic** and **isokinetic** exercise, which can be adapted to meet your training needs. In order to maintain a supple body, there should also be an element of **flexibility**, which you can achieve by various exercises.

You can combine all these elements to give you a very effective training programme designed to meet your specific needs.

Types of exercise

1 Aerobic

During aerobic exercise, the amount of oxygen taken in and used by your body is sufficient to provide the energy you need, and your pathways for producing energy become more efficient. Aerobic fitness improves your capacity to:

(a) Take in large quantities of air
(b) Forcefully deliver large amounts of blood to the muscles
(c) Carry the oxygen in the blood to all muscle groups efficiently

No matter how specific you wish your training to be, it is essential to work up to a high level of aerobic fitness. Cycling and swimming are good forms of aerobic exercise but running is the most popular.

2 Anaerobic

During anaerobic exercise, the amount of oxygen that your body is able to supply is less than the amount necessary to perform the task.

Anaerobic activity can be performed only for short periods since an 'oxygen debt' is incurred, leading to a build-up of lactic acid in the bloodstream. Usually, the first two or three minutes of intense physical activity is anaerobic and then leads to aerobic exercise.

3 Isometric

An isometric contraction is a muscular contraction exerted against an immovable object, or against the contraction of another muscle or muscles. Isometrics are effective in increasing strength in specific muscles but are limited in terms of general fitness.

When your muscles contract against an immovable resistance and there is no limb movement, the exercise is called isometric ('equal length'). This is only useful for building up certain muscles.

4 Isotonic

Isotonic training involves a full range of movement through progressive strengthening exercises, with or without equipment; most common exercises such as calisthenics and weight training involve isotonic contractions. The most effective isotonic exercises are performed against high resistance, with few repetitions.

Isotonic training gives balanced muscular development because it is performed through a full range of movement, but does not provide much aerobic benefit and so should be combined with other exercises.

Limb movement against a constant load, as occurs in weight training, is called isotonic ('equal tension') since your muscle tension remains fairly constant.

Rules to remember

To make your fitness programme as successful as possible, keep the following points in mind:

1 **Regularity**
2 **Balance**
3 **Progression**
4 **Overload**
5 **Variety**

1 Regularity

Regularity is far more important than the amount of exercise taken; unless you exert yourself regularly you will not succeed. An exercise programme can be considered as 'regular' when it is carried out four to five times a week.

If you take strenuous exercise several days in a row, the glycogen (carbohydrate) stores in your body will be greatly reduced, so make sure you build adequate rest periods into your programme

2 Balance

For total fitness, your programme must include every type of exercise.

3 Progression

You must train progressively and use all your muscle groups; do not try harsher exercises until you can do the easy ones.

4 Overload

Your body will adapt to the amount of stress you place upon it. You must work your cardiovascular and muscular systems up to at least 50 per cent of their capacity to improve – this is called 'overload'. You should include enough overload to provide a challenge, but you should not become exhausted.

5 Variety

Include as much variety as possible in your programme; otherwise you may get bored and lose interest. Fitness training is hard work, and to stay motivated over a long period of time you should be constantly trying new ways of keeping fit.

Variety is the spice of an exercise programme; repetitive training can quickly put you off. These outdoor exercise areas, popular in Europe and the USA, offer a wide choice of activity and they are now beginning to appear in facilities in the UK.

5 Isokinetic

Isokinetic or resistance exercises combine the principles of both isometric and isotonic exercises, and usually need special equipment, as found in modern fitness or sports clubs. This equipment is designed to increase the amount of resistance as your muscle pressure increases.

Certain weight machines provide isokinetic ('equal speed') exercise, in which muscle length and the load both vary during the movement.

6 Flexibility

Unless you regularly carry out flexibility exercises, your joints and muscles will lose their elasticity and become stiff. This can cause aching, particularly in the lower back.

Passive stretching exercises are the most effective; you stretch various muscles as far as possible and then hold them in position for varying periods.

In isokinetic exercise the resistance increases as your muscle pressure builds up. While swimming, water resistance increases the harder you push against it.

Flexibility exercises are very important in staving off the slow stiffening of the joints that tends to occur when they are not fully exercised.

Battle Fitness Programme No.6

WORK-OUT:
STARTING THE TEN WEEK CHALLENGE

This is your chance to get to the peak of fitness! The 10-week challenge is designed for all levels of fitness, and does not require a gymnasium or special equipment. All you need is willpower and the determination to see it through to the end.

You have done the fitness tests, and have a good idea of how fit (or unfit) you are at present. Don't forget that you can make very good progress over a short period of time.

To win the Green Beret you must be very fit but everyone has to start somewhere and there is no reason why you cannot increase your own fitness.

The 10-week challenge

Exercise work-outs:
Monday/Wednesday/Friday

Runs:
Tuesday/Thursday

Exercises Remember to rest between sets, e.g. 7 pull-ups – rest – 7 pull-ups – rest – 7 pull-ups. Do the exercises in the order shown, and if possible work with a buddy so that you can motivate each other.	**Pull-ups**	**Burpees**	**Sit-ups**	**Dorsal**	**Push-ups**	**Run**
Level 1 (low)						
Week 1	4+4+4	15+15+15	15+15+15	15+15+15	15+15+15	2-mile run/walk
Week 2	4+4+4	15+15+15	15+15+15	15+15+15	15+15+15	2-mile run
Level 2 (average)						
Week 3	7+7	20+20	20+20	20+20	20+20	3-mile run/walk
Week 4	7+7	20+20	20+20	20+20	20+20	3-mile run
Week 5	7+7+7	20+20+20	20+20+20	20+20+20	20+20+20	4-mile run/walk
Week 6	7+7+7	20+20+20	20+20+20	20+20+20	20+20+20	4-mile run
Level 3 (high)						
Week 7	10+10	25+25	25+25	25+25	25+25	5-mile run/walk
Week 8	10+10	25+25	25+25	25+25	25+25	5-mile run
Week 9	10+10+10	25+25+25	25+25+25	25+25+25	25+25+25	6-mile run/walk
Week 10	10+10+10	25+25+25	25+25+25	25+25+25	25+25+25	6-mile run

The ideal work-out

The best combination of exercise for most people is **aerobic training**, combined with **isotonic training** and **flexibility exercises**.

Ideally, your exercise period would consist of:
1 A warm-up (5-10 mins)
2 The aerobic phase (20 mins)
3 The cool-down (5-10 mins)
4 Muscle strengthening (10-15 mins)
5 Stretching (5-10 mins)

1 A warm-up

Do light exercises to warm your body up and to increase the blood flow to the working muscles. Include some general mobility exercises that put your joints through a full range of movement.

2 The aerobic phase

During this phase you should start very gently and aim for **long, slow, distance** (LSD) rather than shorter bursts of intense activity.

You can walk, jog, cycle, row or swim. Most people like to jog because it is convenient and simple. The target distances for jogging are shown in the table, but you should decide on the distance you will do once you have completed the fitness tests.

The aim is to keep your heart and lungs working at a good steady rate. Don't be put off if you cannot achieve the recommended 20-30 minutes at first, but plan your programme according to how you feel. The aerobic phase is the most important part of the work-out.

3 The cool-down

Don't just stop after the aerobic phase; continue to walk around in order to re-circulate your blood and bring your body back to a normal balanced state. Some light arm exercises will help to send your blood, which has pooled in the legs, towards the upper body and the heart.

Starting position for the dorsal raise: lie in a relaxed manner on your stomach with your hands along your back and feet together.

Simultaneously raise your shoulders and legs in a steady movement then slowly lower them and repeat. Do not force your shoulders uncomfortably high.

4 Muscle toning

These exercises need no equipment (except a pull-up bar, if available) and can be done anywhere. Although most of you will want to start at the basic level, you can do more if you wish; your body will tell you when to stop. The most important thing is to do the sessions at least three times a week.

Modern lifestyles do not encourage the development of the sort of upper body strength demanded by rope work and you may find that pull-ups and push-ups will be the hardest exercises. Persevere, it is well worth the effort!

5 Stretching

Always finish off by stretching your muscles and put your body through a full range of movement. This will help you to move freely and to maintain a good body posture.

The 10-week challenge MOTIVATOR

Use this table as a record of your progress over the next ten weeks. Tick each circle when you have completed each work-out	Monday	Tuesday	Wednesday	Thursday	Friday
Level 1 (low)					
Week 1	○	○	○	○	○
Week 2	○	○	○	○	○
Level 2 (average)					
Week 3	○	○	○	○	○
Week 4	○	○	○	○	○
Week 5	○	○	○	○	○
Week 6	○	○	○	○	○
Level 3 (high)					
Week 7	○	○	○	○	○
Week 8	○	○	○	○	○
Week 9	○	○	○	○	○
Week 10	○	○	○	○	○

Firing the FN Fal

The FN FAL, or SLR to the British Army, is one of the most successful post-war rifles, in service with over 90 armies. More than a dozen countries have manufactured the FN under licence, including South Africa: this is a member of the SADF's Bushman Battalion.

The FN FAL was the first rifle issued to the British Army that had not been designed in Britain. When it first appeared, such things as pistol grips, plastic fore-ends and self-loading were something of a novelty, and many British soldiers swore they could never shoot as well with the FAL as they could with the Lee-Enfield. But with practice and increased familiarity the FAL soon became respected as a reliable and accurate weapon, and generations of soldiers who have known no other rifle have been unable to find serious faults in it. Now, with the advent of the new 5.56 mm SA80 rifle, the traditionalists are bemoaning the passing of the FAL, just as we lamented over the Lee-Enfield.

The Australian Army used its own versions of the FN, and many Australians used them in combat in Vietnam. Some removed the flash suppressor and modified their rifles to fire fully automatic.

The search for a reliable semi-automatic military rifle had begun a good deal further back than you might imagine; some armies tested self-loading rifles before World War I. In 1939 Fabrique Nationale of Belgium had almost got it right when war broke out and their design team fled to Britain. They kept on with their design work, and after the war produced a rifle in the traditional form, with full-length wooden stock, called the M49.

Standard cartridge

This was adopted by a number of countries, and the company then decided to try something more modern in appearance, using the same mechanism. At about this time the NATO countries were disputing the size and shape of the future standard cartridge. FN could see that, whatever the outcome, some of the armies were going to be losers and would need a new rifle quickly, so they began designing around the various potential cartridges which were being suggested.

When the 7.62×51mm was standardized, FN had a design ready, and since the British had gambled on their own 7-mm rifle and lost they turned to FN to provide them with a new military rifle.

Fabrique Nationale called it the Fusil Automatique Leger (light automatic rifle), or 'FAL'; the British called it the Self-Loading Rifle or 'SLR'. About 92 other armies adopted it; it was made under licence in half a dozen countries; and it became one of the most successful rifle designs in history.

Gas operation

The FAL is a gas-operated rifle which, in its original form, can be fired single-shot or automatic. The British, Canadian, Dutch and Indian armies preferred not to risk soldiers blasting ammunition off faster than the supply services could truck it up to them, so their rifles do not have the automatic feature. The gas cylinder is above the barrel and carries a short-stroke piston, the rear end of which faces a bolt carrier which holds the bolt. On firing, some of the gas behind the bullet passes through a gas port and drives the piston back; it strikes the bolt carrier a sharp blow, then a spring returns the piston.

The carrier has had sufficient impulse to drive it all the way back in the receiver and, as it moves back, shaped ramps inside the carrier lift the rear of the bolt out of engagement with a locking face in the floor of the receiver.

A British corporal shows off the newly arrived FN, which his battalion evaluated under combat conditions in Malaya during the early 1950s.

One of the most enduring images of the British Army is the SLR held in a 'non-threatening' position by soldiers on the streets of Northern Ireland.

Changing magazines: like most 7.62-mm NATO rifles the FN's magazine holds 20 rounds, as opposed to the 30 rounds in Kalashnikov rifles.

Below: Royal Marines in a patrol base near Mount Kent check their rifles. In the Falklands both sides used their own versions of the FN FAL.

Above: The magazine catch in close-up. When loading, the front part of the magazine should be inserted first and the back rotated upwards.

Inside the FN FAL

Fabrique Nationale's light automatic rifle, the right arm of the free world, has earned a reputation as one of the most successful assault rifle designs of the post-war years. The FAL is gas piston-operated and is chambered for the heavyweight 7.62-mm NATO cartridge. The result is an extremely robust, almost 'soldier-proof' piece of kit.

Piston
When the gases enter the gas cylinder they expand and push this piston back until it strikes the bolt carrier.

Foresight protector

Gas plug

Gas outlet vent

Gas regulator sleeve

Piston spring
This returns the piston to its original position after it hits the bolt carrier.

Flash hider/grenade launcher fitting

Gas port
As the bullet passes this section, some of the propellant gas is diverted into the gas cylinder.

Front sling swivel

Barrel

Handguard

7.62-mm NATO round

Spring for magazine platform

The continued movement of the carrier now pulls the bolt back, ejecting the spent case, until a return spring sends the bolt forward again. On the forward stroke it pushes a cartridge from the box magazine into the chamber, the bolt closes on the base of the cartridge, and the bolt carrier continues forward. As it does so, more ramps inside the carrier thrust the rear end of the bolt down to lock against the prepared face.

On its way back the bolt rolled over a hammer and cocked it. When the trigger is pressed this hammer is released and flies forward to strike the firing pin in the bolt and fire the car-

FNs come in a variety of sizes as each country modified the design slightly. Apart from the Heavy Barrel LMG model, the British SLR is the largest of all the FN FAL rifle versions.

Stripping the FN FAL

1 Remove the magazine, pull back the bolt and check that the feedway and chamber are clear. Let the bolt forward and rotate the take-down lever anti-clockwise to open the rifle.

2 Pull the bolt cover to the rear and remove it from the receiver. Do not press the trigger while the rifle is open.

3 Pull back the rod on the slide and place your fingers under the breech block as it is withdrawn from the body of the rifle.

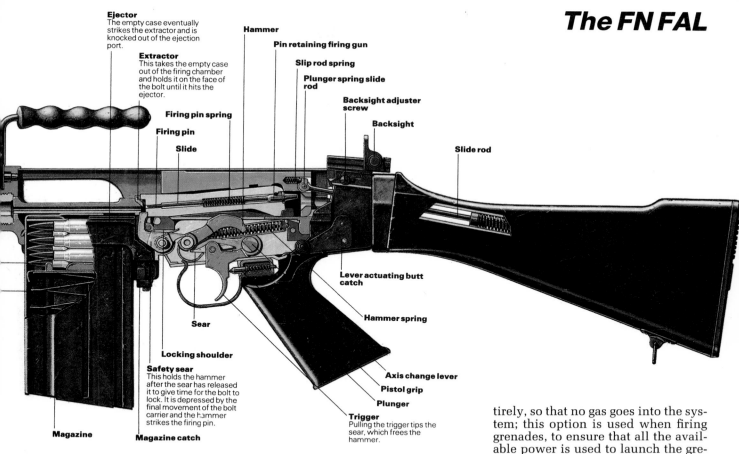

Ejector
The empty case eventually strikes the extractor and is knocked out of the ejection port.

Extractor
This takes the empty case out of the firing chamber and holds it on the face of the bolt until it hits the ejector.

Hammer

Pin retaining firing gun

Slip rod spring

Plunger spring slide rod

Backsight adjuster screw

Backsight

Firing pin spring

Firing pin

Slide

Slide rod

Lever actuating butt catch

Hammer spring

Sear

Locking shoulder

Safety sear
This holds the hammer after the sear has released it to give time for the bolt to lock. It is depressed by the final movement of the bolt carrier and the hammer strikes the firing pin.

Axis change lever

Pistol grip

Plunger

Trigger
Pulling the trigger tips the sear, which frees the hammer.

Magazine

Magazine catch

tridge, starting the whole cycle off again. When firing on automatic, the final movement of the bolt carrier trips a release which frees the hammer, so provided the trigger is kept pressed the rifle will continue to fire.

Sight aperture

The sights vary slightly between different countries, since many armies have their own preferences, but generally speaking the sight is an aperture fitted so that it can be slid along a ramp to give the required elevation. The foresight is a blade set between two prominent protectors at the front of the gas cylinder.

Just below the foresight is the gas regulator which can be adjusted so as to permit more or less gas to flow from the barrel into the gas cylinder, so that when necessary the power can be increased to overcome fouling or dust. The regulator can also be shut off en-

tirely, so that no gas goes into the system; this option is used when firing grenades, to ensure that all the available power is used to launch the grenade. In this use, it is therefore necessary to load and unload the grenade-launching cartridge by manual action.

Box magazine

Ammunition is supplied from a 20-shot detachable box magazine which fits beneath the receiver. Although some early FAL rifles were made in odd calibres to suit special orders, by far the greater proportion of them have been produced in the standard

4 Lift out the breech block by its front end. The firing pin and its retaining pin are then removed along with the lower part of the extractor.

5 Next you remove the gas parts: use a round to push in the wide end of the plunger, turn the plug a quarter-circle downwards and remove it and the piston.

6 Remove the piston and piston spring, which completes the basic strip. Pay particular attention to the gas plug when cleaning the weapon.

7.62 mm NATO calibre.

The British model varies from the standard FAL in some minor details, largely to suit British manufacturing methods but also in having prominent oblique cuts in the bolt carrier which are intended to scour away any dust or dirt inside the receiver and eject it through the ejection opening as the bolt moves back and forth. The Australian Army devised a slightly shorter version than standard, by modifying the barrel and flash hider; they also use the heavy-barrel model as a

Taking aim: the SLR has a longer effective range than any 5.56-mm weapon, because its heavier bullet is less affected by the wind.

Battlefield Evaluation: comparing

FN FAL

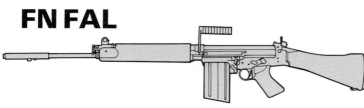

Comparisons between the FN FAL and other service rifles are apt to be misleading because of the difference in calibre. It is not very profitable to compare the FAL with the AK-47 or AKM, for example, since the other two take a smaller cartridge and the FAL can outshoot them any day of the week. The FAL compares very favourably with any other semi-automatic rifle firing 7.62-mm ammunition and is still a good choice for infantrymen fighting in open terrain such as the Falklands or deserts, where firefights can take place at very long ranges.

Specification:
Cartridge: 7.62 mm×51 NATO
Weight: 5 kg
Length: 1143 mm
Cyclic rate of fire: 650 rounds per minute (automatic versions)
Magazine: 20-round box
Effective range: 700 m

Assessment
Reliability   ★★★
Accuracy   ★★★
Age   ★★★★★
Worldwide users   ★★★★★

Although major armies are adopting smaller-calibre rifles, the FN FAL will remain in service for many years.

M14

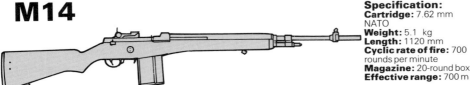

This is really no more than the World War II American Garand rifle with its defect cleared up. The old eight-round clip is replaced by a 20-round box magazine and the gas actuation system modified to improve accuracy and give less violent functioning. Like the Garand, the M14 is a big handful, but it is comfortable and accurate when firing single shots. As an automatic it becomes difficult to control unless you have the light machine-gun version, which has a bipod.

Specification:
Cartridge: 7.62 mm NATO
Weight: 5.1 kg
Length: 1120 mm
Cyclic rate of fire: 700 rounds per minute
Magazine: 20-round box
Effective range: 700 m

Assessment
Reliability   ★★★
Accuracy   ★★★
Age   ★★★★★
Worldwide users   ★★★★★

When the US Marines first took the offensive against the Viet Cong they were armed with the M14.

Simonov SKS

The only self-loading rifle in the Warsaw Pact armies, the SKS is not strictly comparable with the FAL since, like the Kalashnikov, it fires the 7.62-mm×39 cartridge. It weighs less than the standard FAL but the smaller cartridge means that the recoil feels about the same, and the SKS's long barrel extracts as much accuracy from the cartridge as possible, although not much can be expected over 400 metres. The FN FAL can shoot rings around it.

Specification:
Cartridge: 7.62 mm×39
Weight: 3.85 kg (empty)
Length: 1021 mm
Cyclic rate of fire: single shot
Magazine: 10-round internal magazine
Effective range: 400 m

Assessment
Reliability   ★★★
Accuracy   ★★
Age   ★★★★★
Worldwide users   ★★

The SKS was an unsatisfactory half-way house between the assault rifle and traditional weapons.

light machine-gun substitute for units other than infantry.

The Canadian Army version had an aperture in the receiver cover through which the magazine could be replenished by stripping chargers of five rounds down past the open bolt. Brazil has begun making a more or less full-sized FAL but chambered for the 5.65 mm cartridge. The number of variations is legion, but all are matters of detail; the basic FAL remains the same, whatever the national preferences might be.

Like the SA80 and the AKM, the FAL has a heavy-barrelled version that serves as a light machine-gun. With a fixed stock and folding bipod, it weighs an extra 1.75 kg.

the FN FAL with its rivals

Heckler & Koch G3

This is one of the few rifles firing a full-sized cartridge and working on delayed blowback using the roller-delayed system perfected by Heckler & Koch, and used in most of their weapons. Slightly heavier than the FAL, the G3's accuracy and overall performance is so similar as to be indistinguishable in average hands. With a few notable exceptions the G3 has been adopted everywhere the FAL missed.

Specification:
Cartridge: 7.62 mm×51 NATO
Weight: 5.1 kg
Length: 1025 mm
Cyclic rate of fire: 500-600 rounds per minute
Magazine: 20-round box
Effective range: 600 m

Assessment
Reliability ***
Accuracy ***
Age ****
Worldwide users ****

The Heckler & Koch G3 was the FN FAL's biggest rival in 7.62-mm NATO, and has proved almost as popular.

CETME Modelo 58

Many of the design team which worked on the World War II German assault rifle moved to Spain after the war and continued to develop their work. The result was the CETME assault rifle, a 'cheap and cheerful' weapon which is easy to manufacture and simple to shoot. The West Germans acquired some 400 CETMEs in 1956 and the design was developed further by Heckler & Koch to produce the G3. Early CETMEs fired a lighter cartridge than the common 7.62-mm NATO, but this was abandoned in 1964.

Specification:
Cartridge: 7.62 mm NATO
Weight: 4.5 kg
Length: 1016 mm
Cyclic rate of fire: 600 rounds per minute
Magazine: 20-round box
Effective range: 600 m

Assessment
Reliability ***
Accuracy ***
Age *****
Worldwide users *

The CETME was designed to be cheap and easy to produce. The design was developed further by Heckler & Koch.

MAS 49/56

Still in service with some units of the French army and in former French colonies, the MAS 49/56 was one of the first weapons to use direct gas action: some of the propellant gas produced on firing is fed back via a tube and acts directly on the bolt carrier. This type of system can produce excessive fouling, but the MAS 49/56 does not suffer unduly. Some weapons were modified to fire 7.62-mm NATO but the majority are chambered for the French 7.5-mm cartridge.

Specification:
Cartridge: 7.5 mm×54
Weight: 4.5 kg
Length: 1010 mm
Cyclic rate of fire: single shot
Magazine: 10-round box
Effective range: 600 m

Assessment
Reliability ***
Accuracy ***
Age *****
Worldwide users **

The French clung to their unique 7.5-mm round, ensuring that the MAS 49/56 had little export potential.

T-72: Race to the Rhine

The T-72 is one of the great success stories of modern tank history. Fast, reliable yet relatively cheap to construct, over 8,500 T-72s are presently in service with the Red Army alone and models are now being built not only by Soviet state arsenals but also under licence in Czechoslovakia, Poland, India and Yugoslavia. Within the Warsaw Pact East Germany operates 300 T-72s; Bulgaria and Czechoslovakia 200 each; and Poland a further 220. Modified versions, usually with less sophisticated gunnery control and NBC (Nuclear Biological and Chemical) filtration systems, form the nucleus of Syrian and Libyan armoured regiments, whilst the small number of T-72s of the Iraqi army continue to play a significant part in the Iran-Iraq War.

Design History

Since the advent of the T-34/85 early in World War II Soviet main battle tanks have always been built to a cheap, rugged design encompassing good firepower, mobility and armoured protection. Easy to maintain, they have required little support and only a minimum of crew training. However, until recently they were no match for larger and more powerful NATO adversaries such as the British Chieftain, the West German Leopard 1 or United States M 60, and were forced to rely for success on sheer weight of numbers.

An East German T-72 trundles over a temporary bridge carrying KMT-5 mine clearing equipment. Careful design and the use of an automatic loader instead of a fourth crewman gives the T-72 a very low profile.

Established tactics changed drastically when, in 1970, early models of the revolutionary T-64 entered service with the Soviet 3rd Shock Army based in East Germany. The T-72 followed soon after, and after much speculation both tanks have now been joined by the still largely secret T-80 to provide the Soviet Union with a trio of MBTs as good as any in the world.

According to *The Military Balance 1986-87*, published recently by the International Institute of Strategic Studies, of the staggering 53,000 tanks in service with the Soviet Union 9,300 are T-64s, 8,500 are T-72s and 1,400 are T-80s.

Fire power

The T-72 has considerable potential firepower. The RAPIRER 3 125-mm smoothbore main gun fires APFSDS (Armour Piercing Fin Stabilised Discarding Sabot), HEAT (High Explosive Anti Tank) and HE projectiles, is fully stabilised, and unlike earlier Soviet tank guns can fire accurately on the move. The APFSDS projectile, with its estimated muzzle velocity of some 1,700 metres per second, has an effective range of 2,100 metres, is superior to the British L11 120-mm gun fitted to Chieftain and Challenger, and is a probable match for the much-vaunted West German Rheinmetall 120-mm smoothbore gun operational with Leopard 2 and now retrofitted to later models of the United States M1 Abrams.

The integrated fire control system with its laser rangefinder and on-board ballistic computer is fitted to all but the earliest T-72 models. This not only relieves the gunner and commander of some of their traditional tasks, but greatly increases the probability of a first-round hit.

Most revolutionary of all is the carousel-type automatic loader based on the tried and tested BMP Armoured Personnel Carrier system, which enables a reduction in the crew to three men. Twenty-four rounds of assorted ammunition, designed with separate propellant cartridge and projectile, are carried in the carousel itself, whilst a further 16 rounds are stored uncomfortably in the already cramped crew compartment.

The commander selects the required round by pressing a button, after which the carousel rotates to the nearest suitable projectile and stops. The gunner then lifts the cassette and the round is rammed into the breech. An automatic ejection system for the propellant casing completes the cycle.

Although simple in design, this system is not without its problems. The autoloader is unreliable and when it fails manual loading takes a great deal of time, and can only be carried out at some risk to the gunner's fingers. NATO designers have steadfastly ignored all temptations to reduce crew size by the introduction of automatic loading despite acute shortages of trained manpower, as they accept that manual loading is far more reliable and, in the case of a good crew, only a little slower. So it is likely that, whatever they say to the contrary, the Soviets removed the loader only because it would otherwise have been impossible to fit so large a gun into so small a turret, and not for any reasons of efficiency.

Fast, low and agile, the T-72 is a very effective Main Battle Tank, which will equip the majority of Warsaw Pact tank formations while elite Soviet units receive the T-64 and T-80 in much smaller numbers. This is the T-72M1 which has thicker armour on the turret and hull front. A layer of GRP on the turret top increases protection against top attack weapons and nuclear radiation.

The T-72 does not represent the latest in Soviet tank technology like the T-80. It was specifically designed for production on a massive scale for the Warsaw Pact armies and Soviet Allies.

Inside the T-72

Although at 41,000kg the T-72 is the largest and heaviest tank in Soviet service, its wide tracks and improved suspension allow it to traverse all but the boggiest of terrain.

All T-72s are fitted with a dozer blade under the glacis plate and can be fitted with the KMT4/6 mine roller/plough system, three of which are carried with each tank company. A snorkel can be fitted to enable the tank to ford rivers to a depth of 5.5 metres, but preparation takes up to 45 minutes and extensive engineering preparation to the banks is needed.

Radiation sensor

NBC protection is provided by the PAZ system. A radiation detector, located on the right side of the turret compartment, senses the initial pulse of radiation from a blast and activates a number of explosive squibs or spring-loaded shutters which close the engine louvres, sight apertures, vents and air intakes to the blower/dust separator.

Although notionally this relieves the crew from the necessity of wearing hot and cumbersome protective suits, many personnel will still choose to do so in case any part of the chassis is holed and the airtight seal broken. Also, the commander will not be able to operate the anti-air machine-gun and his vision will be severely limited.

Armour protection

Soviet armour protection improved considerably with the coming of the T-64, and several refinements have been incorporated. The most important new addition was the glacis plate set at a very shallow angle directly

Of the new generation of Soviet MBTs represented by the T-64, T-72 and T-80, the T-72 is the only one to have been exported. Consequently far more is known about its capabilities, and the Soviet press, with its eye on the export market, has been much freer with technical details.

125-mm gun
Stabilized to fire on the move, the 125-mm gun fires APFSDS, HEAT and HE. The APFSDS round has a muzzle velocity of over 1600 metres per second and can penetrate and destroy any tank not fitted with advanced armour at ranges of up to 2000 metres.

Engine
The T-72's power-to-weight ratio is significantly better than that of the T-62 or T-54, and it is an agile Main Battle Tank. Its only weakness is that the cooling fan positioned at the back of the engine compartment is not very effective and over-heating remains a consistent problem.

Running gear
The T-72's running gear is a major factor in its high battlefield mobility. Earlier Soviet MBTs only had road wheels, but the T-72 has track support rollers. The torsion bar suspension gives much better shock absorption.

Infra-red searchlight
Only useful out to about 800 metres, the IR searchlight is elevated and depressed with the gun. It is of limited value since it betrays the tank's position at night and is vulnerable to shell splinters and small-arms fire.

below the driver's hatch. This is capable of defeating a short-fused TOW 1 or LAW round and might even cause a SABOT round to bounce off the front of the hull, but would have little effect against a clean strike from a TOW 2 missile.

Automatic loader

Using an automatic loader cuts the crew to three, saving a lot of space in the fighting compartment. The commander chooses the ammunition type and the rotating magazine under the turret basket turns to bring a full ammunition rack under the ammunition hoist. The ammunition comes in two parts, the charge being stored above the actual projectile.

125-mm smoothbore gun

propulsion charge
projectile
turret floor

commander's position
carousel loader
125-mm projectiles

charges

gunner's position

Early model T-72s incorporated spring loaded 'gull wings' along the side of the chassis to protect the wheels and tracks. Theoretically these steel plates would stick out at an angle of 45° from the side of the tank, causing the premature detonation of an incoming TOW round before it hits the hull, but although fine in theory this was found to be ineffective in practice and full-length skirts have now been fitted to most tanks.

Direct hit vulnerability

In recent fighting in the Lebanon several Syrian T-72s were destroyed with comparative ease by Israeli tanks and anti-tank missiles, and so it is clear that the T-72 is still vulnerable to a direct hit. But it is small, fast and has a remarkably low profile, making a direct hit difficult to obtain.

The Soviets have apparently made no attempt to fit their revolutionary new reactive armour to the T-72, preferring to concentrate this considerably-enhanced protection on the later T-80s and on a few T-64Bs. Although reactive armour is still secret in detail, it is obvious from photographs that each separate armour piece is

Commander
The commander's cupola traverses independently of the turret; he cannot engage targets by himself, but he can bring the turret, and hence the gun, to bear on his line of sight. He operates the radio and the 12.7-mm machine-gun as well as commanding the vehicle.

Lead foam NBC protection
On Soviet but not export models of the T-72, the fighting compartment is lined with a 40 to 80-mm thick layer of foam plastic impregnated with lead to protect the crew from nuclear radiation.

Gunner
The gunner lays the gun electro-hydraulically with a two-handed controller. A fire control computer calculates the gun elevation angle. Night fighting capability is weak, since the gunner has no way to measure range with his night sight.

Driver
Unlike modern NATO tanks, the T-72 does not have automatic power-shift transmission or modern steering. The driver has to change gear using a clutch and a power-assisted gear lever and steer the vehicle with two steering levers.

Frontal glacis
The well-shaped glacis of the T-72 is believed to be protected by some 200 mm of multi-layer armour. Additional armour is positioned underneath the gun cradle.

Digging attachment
This has to be lowered by hand and enables the T-72 to dig its own hull-down position. Depending on the state of the soil, this takes between 10 and 20 minutes. The attachment also provides additional protection for the hull front.

Track
Like the modernized T-62s, the T-72 has a single-pin track with rubber pads, 58 cm wide. 4.43 m of track are in contact with the ground, giving a low ground pressure of only 0.8 kg/cm².

approximately the size of a house brick, and consists of two sheets of metal with a small explosive charge between.

Force dissipation

Any shell or missile hitting the outer sheet of metal will activate the charge, which will dissipate a large percentage of the destructive forces of the hostile explosion. The crew will be shaken but unharmed, and the tank itself can carry on fighting. Reactive armour is easy to fit and comparatively cheap to produce, so it will probably be fitted to the T-72s in the next couple of years.

There are several variants of the T-72 of which the T-72M is the most numerous: in fact, many tanks origi-

The T-72M, distinguished by having the searchlight on the right rather than the left of the main gun, entered series production in 1980 and has a laser rangefinder rather than the less effective optical equipment fitted to first T-72s.

Weapons and Equipment Guide

nally designated 'T-80' are now conceded to be nothing but T-72 variants. Tanks sold to friendly Arab States were deliberately denuded of all classified innovations, particularly the complex integrated fire-control system, which was replaced with a more traditional coincidence range-finder.

Dust screen

Gull wing side plates were fitted in preference to side skirts on the interesting premise that in a desert environment the lack of side skirts would result in the tank wheels throwing up considerable dust, which would itself act as a screen against potential enemy missile aimers.

The T-72M, now in production in Poland and Czechoslovakia as well as the Soviet Union, has side skirting, smoke grenade launchers, an enlarged view finder, external ammunition boxes for the storage of additional machine-gun rounds (previously only seen on the T-64), and a marked bulge in the forward right quarter of the turret presumed to contain enhanced optic equipment.

A column of early model T-72s on exercise in the Soviet Union: the combination of T-72s, T-64s and T-80s has substantially improved the quality of Soviet armour based in Eastern Europe.

Battlefield Evaluation: comparing

T-72

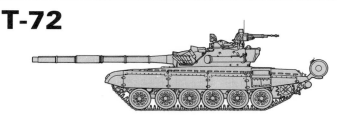

The T-72 is in large-scale production, equipping first- and second-line Soviet tank divisions and replacing the obsolete T-54/5s still in widespread Warsaw Pact service. It is not the equal of the latest NATO MBTs, but its agility, low profile and powerful main armament make it superior to older vehicles such as the Leopard 1, M48 to M60A1, and AMX-30. Successive variants of the T-72 have improved frontal protection and reactive armour to defend them against infantry anti-tank weapons.

Specification:
Crew: 3
Combat weight: 41 tonnes
Road speed: 60 km/h
Power-to-weight ratio: 19 hp/tonne
Length: 6.95 m
Height: 2.37 m
Armament: 1×125-mm smoothbore gun; 1×12.7-mm machine-gun; 1×7.62-mm machine-gun

Assessment
Firepower   ★★★★
Protection   ★★★
Age   ★★★
Worldwide users   ★★★

Now uparmoured and with improved rangefinding equipment, the T-72 is a first-class Main Battle Tank.

M1 Abrams

The M1 is a much more capable tank than the T-72; it is better at firing on the move, and its night-fighting capability will remain substantially superior until the Soviets fit their tanks with high-performance thermal imagers. Advanced armour gives the M1 better protection against both HEAT and APFDS rounds, and its exceptional power-to-weight ratio makes the M1 at least as agile as the lighter Soviet MBTs.

Specification:
Crew: 4
Combat weight: 54.5 tonnes
Road speed: 72 km/h
Power-to-weight ratio: 27 hp/tonne
Length: 7.9 m
Height: 2.37 m
Armament: 1×120-mm gun; 1×50-cal machine-gun; 1×7.62-mm machine-gun

Assessment
Firepower   ★★★★★
Protection   ★★★★★
Age   ★★★
Worldwide users   ★

The M1 Abrams is substantially more capable but correspondingly more expensive than the T-72.

Challenger

Like the M1 Abrams, the British Challenger is better armoured and better armed than the T-72. Better fire control systems, night-fighting equipment and advanced armour give the Challenger substantial advantages, but the T-72 was designed for production on a colossal scale to replace the vast tank fleet of obsolete vehicles in the Warsaw Pact. The Soviets also produce the much more capable but much more expensive T-64 and T-80, which equip their tank units in East Germany and are not for export.

Specification:
Crew: 4
Combat weight: 62 tonnes
Road speed: 56 km/h
Power-to-weight ratio: 19 hp/tonne
Length: 8.3 m
Height: 2.9 m
Armament: 1×120-mm gun; 2×7.62-mm machine-gun

Assessment
Firepower   ★★★★★
Protection   ★★★★★
Age   ★
Worldwide users   ★

Like the M1, the British Challenger is individually superior to the T-72, thanks to better armour and electronics.

The future

Although the newer T-80 is in full production within the Soviet Union, up to 2,000 T-72s per year are still being produced and this is likely to continue for the foreseeable future. Although the small size of the tank coupled with the unreliability of the automatic loader lead to rapid crew fatigue, and a penetrating hit anywhere will almost certainly kill it, the T-72 is nevertheless extremely competitive.

The T-72 will remain in service for many years and will provide the backbone of Soviet and Warsaw Pact tank strength to the end of the century.

the T-72 with its rivals

M60

The M60 still forms a substantial proportion of US tank strength and is barely equal to the T-72 in many respects. It is no better armoured than the T-72 but is nearly a third higher, making it a substantially larger target. The 105-mm gun can knock out T-72s – the Israelis proved this in Lebanon – but subsequent NATO and Warsaw Pact MBTs carry larger and more powerful weapons, and it remains to be seen whether the M60 will receive an 120-mm gun or improved 105-mm ammunition.

Specification: (M60A3)
Crew: 4
Combat weight: 52.5 tonnes
Road speed: 48 km/h
Power-to-weight ratio: 14 hp/tonne
Length: 6.9 m
Height: 3.27 m
Armament: 1×105-mm gun; .50-cal machine-gun; 1×7.62-mm machine-gun

Assessment
Firepower ★★★★
Protection ★★★
Age ★★★★
Worldwide users ★★★

Despite its age and serious weaknesses, the M60 is still used in large numbers by the US Army.

Type 69-II

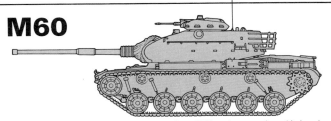

Chinese military equipment has lagged far behind the Soviet Union and the West but its latest MBT, the Type 69-II, is part of an extensive modernization programme. While the PLA still depends on the obsolete Type 59, the Type 69 features fully stabilized armament, an improved fire control system and a laser rangefinder. China has supplied a good number of Type 69s to the Iraqis and it will be interesting to see how they perform in the interminable Gulf War.

Specification:
Crew: 4
Combat weight: 37 tonnes
Road speed: 50 km/h
Power-to-weight ratio: 16 hp/tonne
Length: 6.2 m
Height: 2.8 m
Armament: 1×100-mm smoothbore; 1×12.7-mm and 2×7.62-mm machine-guns

Assessment
Firepower ★★★
Protection ★★
Age ★★
Worldwide users ★★

The Type 69-II is a great improvement on earlier Chinese tanks but is still unequal to the T-72.

OF-40

Closely resembling and, indeed, using many parts from the Leopard 1, the OF-40 is an Italian tank aimed at the international market, but so far only a handful have been sold to the United Arab Emirates. The OF-40 is armed only with a 105-mm gun, but has modern fire control systems and a laser rangefinder. Its modest armour protection is inferior to that of the later models of T-72.

Specification:
Crew: 4
Combat weight: 45.5 tonnes
Road speed: 60 km/h
Power-to-weight ratio: 18 hp/tonne
Length: 6.8 m
Height: 2.45 m
Armament: 1×105-mm gun; 2×7.62-mm machine-guns

Assessment
Firepower ★★★
Protection ★★
Age ★★
Worldwide users ★

The OF-40 was produced for export by OTO-Melara and FIAT but has attracted no significant sales.

TOW: Tank Menace

TOW stands for 'Tube-launched, Optically-tracked, Wire-guided'; and the TOW anti-tank missile is probably the most successful and widely-distributed anti-tank missile in the Western world. Over 250,000 have been made and they are in service with 25 armies. Moreover, TOW can claim to be one of the few modern anti-armour weapons that has actually been proved in combat, having been used very successfully by the Israelis in various campaigns as well as by the US Army in Vietnam.

TOW was developed by the Hughes Aircraft Corporation, in response to a request from the US Army for a more modern weapon to replace the 106-mm recoilless rifle as the USA's primary anti-tank defence. Work began in 1965 and development was completed very rapidly, and the missile went into service in 1970.

Israeli success

Shortly afterwards it was exported to Israel, and used in the 1973 Yom Kippur War. It has been used by them several times since, and the Israeli army has proved that it can defeat a Russian T-72 tank in frontal attack; something that nobody expected it to do.

Originally mounted on jeeps, TOW has since been fitted to the M113 APC, to helicopters, to a special version of the M113 known as 'TUA' for 'TOW

TOW is really too heavy to be used in the same way as MILAN or the Soviet copy 'Spigot'. Mounting it on a light vehicle produces a mobile tank destroying system with no protection.

Under Armour', or 'ITV' for 'Improved TOW Vehicle'; and it forms part of the armament of the M2 Bradley Infantry Fighting Vehicle. It is used by the British Army on the Westland Lynx helicopter, by the West Germans on the BO-105 and by the Italians on the Agusta A109.

TOW is a 'second generation' anti-tank missile, which means that the operator does not have to steer it to the target; he merely has to keep his sight aligned with the target and the missile itself stays on course. The launcher unit consists of a tripod, a glass-fibre reinforced plastic launch tube, sight unit and a guidance computer unit. The missile is delivered in a sealed launcher/container, and this is simply dropped into the open-topped rear end of the launcher, where it automatically makes the necessary connections.

Two exhausts

The operator takes aim through the sight and fires. A solid-fuel booster rocket burns for 0.05 of a second and ejects the missile from its container, down the launch tube, and on its way. After a few metres of flight the sustainer or flight rocket motor ignites and accelerates the missile to its maximum speed of 360 metres per second. This flight motor exhausts through two nozzles at the side of the missile body, an arrangement which prevents

TOW is a very versatile missile. Launched from helicopters, vehicles or a tripod mounting, it is the most powerful ATGM in widespread service. Here it is fired from a Hughes 500 Defender.

interference with the guidance flare in the missile tail.

This flare is easily seen from the rear, and while the operator keeps his sight on the target, tracking it as necessary, the missile flies into the field of view and the flare becomes visible. An infra-red sensor inside the sight identifies the flare and measures its location relative to the axis of the sight.

Flight correction

If there is any deviation – as there inevitably will be in the initial stages of flight – the guidance computer calculates what correction is required to fly the missile into the sight line and sends the necessary instructions, as electrical impulses, down two thin wires that are being unreeled from the missile as it flies. These corrections are applied to the control fins, so that the missile steers into alignment with the sight.

The position of the flare is constantly monitored and corrections are constantly flowing down the wire, so that within a very few seconds of flight the missile is more or less stable on the sight axis and will, therefore, impact the target exactly where the operator has laid his sight cross-wires.

By fitting **TOW** to the Bradley Infantry Fighting Vehicle, the **US** Army has ensured that its infantry sections are able to take out any armoured vehicle on the battlefield. On the other hand, the vehicle must remain stationary to fire its missile, which would be embarrassing if the target is a T-64 shooting back 125-mm APDSFS rounds at five times the speed of sound.

The tripod ground mounting for **TOW** is a forbidding size and weight, preventing infantry from using it as a mobile weapon during an attack. However, it is a superb defensive weapon with a very long range and enormous killing power.

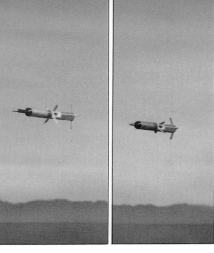

TOW 2 blasts off towards the target: (1) the launch motor fires; (2) wings and tail pop out into position and the nose probe begins to extend; (3) probe wings and tail are fully deployed; (4) flight motor ignites.

It is claimed that, in some tens of thousands of firings, the weapon has shown a 93 per cent record of direct hits, and most of the failures have been due to operator faults.

The warhead is a shaped charge, and although no figures are quoted by the manufacturers it should defeat about 400 mm of armour plate. The maximum range of the missile, governed by the length of wire, is 3,750 metres.

Improvements

Since the targets get harder and harder, the US Army has had to demand improvements to TOW in order to keep ahead of possible opposition. The first stage was a new 127-mm diameter warhead, very slightly bigger than the original. A feature of this warhead was an extensible probe carrying the fuse; this was concealed within the warhead until after launch, whereupon it extended forward so that it detonated the warhead just outside the armour, the optimum

Flight motor
Located near the centre of gravity of the missile, the flight motor uses a solid propellant. TOW 2 has a more powerful motor to cope with the increased weight of the warhead. The motor ignites after the missile has travelled 12 metres; any less and it would injure the gunner.

Warhead
The first two versions of TOW were armed with a warhead 127 mm in diameter, but TOW 2's warhead is 152 mm wide and occupies the entire diameter of the missile's body. It is capable of destroying any Main Battle Tank in service.

Gyro
The gyro ensures the missile flies on a steady course, sending correction signals to the control surfaces.

Extendable probe
This extends after the missile has been launched and makes sure that the warhead detonates at the optimum distance away from the target's armour. If the warhead explodes too close to the target's armour, the explosive jet is not properly formed and will not penetrate as far. If it goes off too far away, penetration is similarly reduced.

Gas bottle

Electronics unit

Inside TOW

Safety and arming unit
TOW is armed after it has travelled 65 metres; it cannot be used against a target any closer than this.

TOW is seen here on its infantry mounting, a bulky piece of kit which requires a four-man team to operate it. The missile has proved itself very successful in action from Vietnam to Lebanon and its warhead has been improved to enable it to penetrate the advanced armour fitted to the latest tanks.

Like all anti-tank guided missiles, TOW produces a large backblast; not as big as the flash produced by large-calibre recoilless rifles, but nevertheless a complete giveaway.

position for maximum penetration. This was known as ITOW – Improved TOW.

The next step was TOW 2, a 152-mm warhead; this meant that the warhead was now the full diameter of the missile – earlier warheads had been smaller than the missile body – and since the penetrative power of a shaped charge is more or less proportional to its diameter, this gave a much improved effect on the target. TOW 2 also has the extended probe fuse assembly.

New fuel

With this warhead the guidance system was also improved, using a new digital micro-processor giving better accuracy, and, because of the increased weight of the warhead, the flight motor was provided with a new type of fuel to give more thrust. TOW 2 went into service with the US Army in early 1983, and existing missiles have

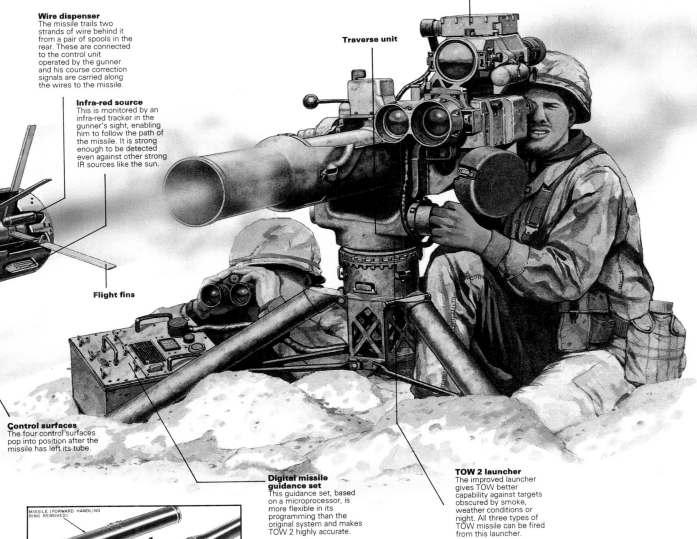

AN/TAS-4 sight
This is used to track targets at night and can be used as a completely independent fire control sensor.

Wire dispenser
The missile trails two strands of wire behind it from a pair of spools in the rear. These are connected to the control unit operated by the gunner and his course correction signals are carried along the wires to the missile.

Traverse unit

Infra-red source
This is monitored by an infra-red tracker in the gunner's sight, enabling him to follow the path of the missile. It is strong enough to be detected even against other strong IR sources like the sun.

Flight fins

Control surfaces
The four control surfaces pop into position after the missile has left its tube.

Digital missile guidance set
This guidance set, based on a microprocessor, is more flexible in its programming than the original system and makes TOW 2 highly accurate.

TOW 2 launcher
The improved launcher gives TOW better capability against targets obscured by smoke, weather conditions or night. All three types of TOW missile can be fired from this launcher.

MISSILE (FORWARD HANDLING RING REMOVED)

LAUNCH TUBE

SIGHT/SENSOR

TRAVERSING UNIT

TRIPOD

GUIDANCE SET

The parts of the ground mount: the total weight of the mount for TOW 2 is 93 kg, and each missile weighs 28 kg. A four-man crew is necessary to carry and operate the ground launcher.

been brought up to TOW 2 standard by fitting the new warhead and other refinements.

Hughes is currently working on a radio-guided version of TOW so as to do away with the trailing wire. The need to unreel the wire restricts the acceleration and speed of the missile and also limits the maximum range. By doing away with it, and substituting a radio link for the guidance commands, Hughes hopes to improve the flight speed and extend the maximum range. Six converted TOW 2 missiles are to be tested late this year, under a

The different versions of TOW: from the left, TOW, Improved TOW and TOW 2. The probe on the nose ensures that the warhead explodes at the optimum distance from the armour.

US Army test programme.

Another approach has been taken by the Israeli army, who have converted some of their TOW missiles to laser beam-riding guidance. In fact, they have gone beyond conversion and are manufacturing their own missiles, but the design certainly shows the TOW parentage in the shape of the missile and its propulsion and warhead systems. The only change is in guidance, which is done by projecting a laser beam from the launcher to the

An M113A2 fires an Improved TOW from its double launcher. The acquisition sight is mounted on top of the elevating arms. With 10 missiles stored in the hull, this is an effective tank destroyer.

Battlefield Evaluation: comparing

TOW

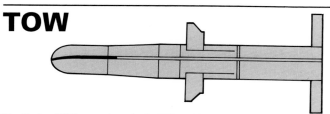

Specification: TOW 2
Missile weight: 28 kg
Launcher weight: 92 kg
Warhead: 5.9-kg shaped-charge HE
Minimum range: 65 m
Maximum range: 3750 m
Armour penetration: 800 mm+

The Hughes TOW entered service in 1970, and from its first combat use against the North Vietnamese army has proved one of the most successful of modern anti-tank weapons. It has seen extensive action in the Middle East, especially in the Yom Kippur war and in the Israeli invasion of the Lebanon, and now equips the armies of as many as 40 countries. TOW's long range and heavy warhead make it a formidable battlefield weapon, but its size and weight mean that it requires a four-man crew when used by the infantry. It is much more suitable to vehicle or to helicopter launch, and most combat use has been in these roles.

Assessment
Reliability ★★★★
Accuracy ★★★★
Age ★★★
Worldwide users ★★★★★

An extravagantly camouflaged US soldier drives a jeep-mounted TOW launcher in South Korea.

HOT

Specification:
Missile weight: 23.5 kg
Launcher weight: (launch tube only) 8.5 kg
Warhead: 6-kg hollow-charge HE
Minimum range: 75 m
Maximum range: 4000 m
Armour penetration: (HOT 2) 1300 mm+

HOT has a similar performance to TOW, and indeed the name means much the same, but in French. The *Haut subsonique, Optiquement, Téléguidé* missile is a second-generation weapon developed jointly by France and Germany by the Euromissile consortium. It is in service with at least 14 countries, including Syria whose army used the helicopter-launched version with some success against the Israelis in Lebanon, and Iraq whose forces have fired HOT from vehicles and helicopters against the Iranians in the long-running Gulf War. The Soviet AT-5 'Spandrel' is very similar to HOT, and may be based on stolen HOT technology.

Assessment
Reliability ★★★★
Accuracy ★★★★★
Age ★★
Worldwide users ★★★

HOT is the Franco-German equivalent to TOW and has similar capability. It was used in combat in Lebanon.

MILAN

Specification:
Missile weight: 11.3 kg
Launcher weight: (control unit and tripod) 16.5 kg
Warhead: 3 kg hollow-charge HE
Minimum range: 25 m
Maximum range: 2000 m
Armour penetration: 1000 mm+

MILAN works in much the same way as TOW, although as it is not strictly comparable. It is much more portable than the heavy American weapon, but its smaller size means that its maximum range is much less. The new warhead introduced in 1984 means that its armour penetration is at least as good as that of the larger missile. More than 200,000 MILANs have been produced since the first technical evaluations in 1971, and it equips some 35 armies around the world. MILAN is a very accurate weapon.

Assessment
Reliability ★★★★
Accuracy ★★★★★
Age ★★★
Worldwide users ★★★★★

MILAN is far more portable than TOW and is almost as powerful, but has a much shorter range.

target. The missile has a sensor mounted in its tail that can detect the laser beam, measure any deviation, and steer the missile back into alignment with the beam. With this system there is no link between the launcher and the missile, and there is no way by which an enemy could jam the guidance, which is a weak point of the Hughes proposal for radio guidance. Moreover, the absence of wire allows the Israeli 'MAPATS' missile to reach a maximum range of 4,500 metres.

TOW is the most successful anti-tank guided missile. Successive improvement programmes have enable it to maintain its effectiveness despite advances in tank armour and battlefield electronics.

the TOW with its rivals

AT-4 'Spigot'

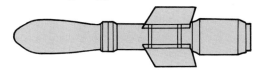

Soviet anti-tank capabilities have been significantly enhanced in the 1980s with the introduction of a number of new ATGWs. The man-portable missile given the NATO reporting name 'Spigot' has also been seen on a vehicle mount along with a larger missile, the AT-5 'Spandrel'. These weapons bear a marked resemblance to the Western MILAN and HOT, and US reports indicate that their design leans heavily on technology stolen from Euromissile. 'Spigot' is in service with the Soviet army, and has been observed with Polish, East German and Czechoslovak units.

Specification:
Missile weight: (estimated) 10-12 kg
Launcher weight: (including missile) 40 kg approx.
Warhead: HEAT (slightly heavier than MILAN
Minimum range: unknown
Maximum range: (approx.) 2000 m
Armour penetration: at least 500 mm, possibly 850 mm or more

Assessment
Reliability	***
Accuracy	****
Age	k*
Worldwide users	**

AT-4 'Spigot' is one of several Soviet anti-tank missiles based on 'acquired' Western technology.

Swingfire

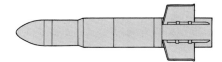

Swingfire is the British equivalent to TOW. It utilises a similar guidance system, allied to an even larger warhead capable of penetrating all current armour types. First entering service in 1969, Swingfire is mounted on the Striker armoured vehicles of the British and Belgian armies. A palletised version is built under licence in Egypt, which can be mounted on any vehicle or trainer of Land Rover size or larger. In separated fire mode the operator's sight can be connected to the launcher by a separation cable up to 100 m in length.

Specification:
Missile weight: 27 kg
Launcher box weight: 10 kg
Warhead: 7-kg hollow-charge HE
Minimum range: 150 m
Maximum range: 4000 m
Armour penetration: 800 mm+

Assessment
Reliability	***
Accuracy	****
Age	***
Worldwide users	**

Swingfire is the British equivalent to TOW and carries a similarly monstrous warhead.

ADATS

The dual-purpose Air Defence Anti-Tank System, or ADATS, is a joint development by Oerlikon of Switzerland and Martin Marietta of the USA. Designed to cope with fast-moving airborne targets as well as tanks, the ADATS missile is much larger, very much faster and has considerably greater range than other ATGWs. The Mach 3 missile is equipped with both impact and proximity fuses, and is laser-guided. The launch system is equipped with surveillance radar, Forward Looking Infra Red, Low Light TV and a laser rangefinder. ADATS has been selected by the Canadian Armed Forces, although the system's high cost means it is to be used primarily for air-defence.

Specification:
Missile weight: 51 kg
Launcher canister weight: not known
Warhead: dual-purpose 12-kg+ HE
Minimum range: 500 m
Maximum range: (ground) 6000 m; (air) 8000 m
Armour penetration: 900 mm+

Assessment
Reliability	****
Accuracy	*****
Age	*
Worldwide users	*

ADATS can be used against tanks or aircraft but it is an expensive system more likely to be used as a SAM.

Combating the Climate

Eye protection
Wear polarised sunglasses on bright days. As extra protection in wind and snow, you will need goggles.

Cap comforter
Elite units prefer a dark-coloured wool watch cap, but on issue are cold-weather caps with protective flaps. Balaclavas and ski masks are also used, but remember that when your ears are covered your hearing – the first line of defence against the enemy – will be impaired.

Insulation mat
You need this when sleeping or resting to lessen the effects of ground cold on your body.

Thermal clothing
This is your second layer and is ideally a 'duvet' jacket with hood and salopettes. This type of clothing should not be worn when on the move, unless it is extremely cold.

Beltkit and backpack
Most soldiers trained in Arctic warfare prefer to keep their webbing attached to their backpack, rather than over their clothes, which restricts movement. The beltkit should include a metal cup and water bottle so that if your water supply freezes you can melt it over a fire.

Over-whites
The fifth and top layer is a set of lightweight oversmock and trousers. When the weather is not too bad, this can be the top layer, omitting the camouflage smock and waterproofs.

Backpack cover
This is waterproof nylon, white for camouflage; sometimes it is reversible, with green on the other side, so that it can be used in tundra or forest conditions.

Mitts
Must be worn to prevent frostbite, and especially when you have to touch anything metal. Mitts have a special trigger finger so that it can fire your weapon. Link one mitt to the other by a cord through the sleeves of your smock so that you can take them off without losing them.

Underclothing
This should be a polypropylene shirt and pants; the material allows ventilation, the zip is shielded from the skin, the cuffs can be extended over your wrists, and a broad tail on the shirt prevents a gap when you bend over.

Waterproof clothing
This fourth layer should ideally be made of Goretex, which is waterproof but allows body heat condensation to escape. It should not be the top layer when the temperature is at or below freezing point because escaping condensation will form an ice shell that will lower your body temperature.

Combat shell clothing
The third layer is usually a windproofed camouflaged smock and trousers, loose and baggy and so trapping a layer of 'dead' air that is warmed by your body. The trouser legs open on the outside from ankle to knee to permit them to be removed without taking your boots off.

Socks
Feet must be kept dry; wet socks should be changed as soon as possible and dried.

Boots
These should be well insulated and should preferably be sealed with Goretex gaiters. Wash the boots inside and out once a month.

Snowshoes
Best used with ski poles; these make walking easier.

Clothing for cold

You must not only have enough clothing to protect you from the cold; you must also know how to get the most warmth from it.

There are four basic principles you should follow to keep warm.

1 Wear your clothing loose and in layers
Wearing too-tight clothing and footgear restricts the circulation of the blood and invites cold injury. It also decreases the volume of air trapped between the layers, reducing its insulating value.

Several layers of lightweight clothing are better than one equally thick layer of clothing, because the layers have dead air space between them which provides extra insulation. In addition, layers of clothing allow you to take off or add bits to prevent excessive sweating or to increase warmth.

2 Avoid overheating
When you get too hot, you sweat and your clothing absorbs the moisture. This affects your warmth in two ways: dampness decreases the insulating quality of clothing, and as sweat evaporates your body cools.

Adjust your clothing so that you do not sweat. You can do this by partially opening your parka or jacket, by removing an inner layer of clothing, by removing heavy mittens, or by throwing back your parka hood or changing to lighter head cover. The head and hands act as efficient heat dissipators when overheated.

3 Keep clothing dry
In cold temperatures, your inner layers of clothing can become wet from sweat and your outer layer, if not water-repellent, can become wet from snow and frost melted by body heat.

Wear water-repellent outer clothing, if available. It will shed most of the water collected from melting snow and frost. Before entering a heated shelter, brush off the snow and frost.

Despite the precautions you take, there will be times when you cannot avoid getting wet. At such times, drying your clothing may become a major problem. On the march, hang your damp mittens and socks on your pack: sometimes the wind and sun will dry this clothing. Or you can put damp socks or mittens, unfolded, near your body so that your body heat can dry them.

In bivouac, hang damp clothing inside the tent near the top, using drying lines or improvised racks. You may even be able to dry each item by holding it before an open fire. Dry leather items slowly. If no other means are available for drying your boots, put them between the sleeping bag shell and liner. Your body heat will help to dry the leather.

4 Keep clothing clean
This is always important from the standpoint of sanitation and comfort; in winter, it is also important for warmth. Clothes matted with dirt and grease lose much of their insulation quality. If the air pockets in clothing are crushed or filled up, heat can escape from the body more readily.

A heavy down-lined sleeping bag is one of the most valuable pieces of survival gear in cold weather. Make sure the down remains dry. If wet, it loses a lot of its insulation value.

Survival in Arctic and sub-Arctic conditions is survival against constant attack. Day and night, without respite, the cold lays siege to your body. There is no let-up; staying alive requires attention to detail for 24 hours a day. Clothes, shelter and food are your major weapons against the cold – plus a strong will to survive. Without the will, the battle is already lost.

Air temperatures of −40°C and wind velocities of 30 knots are common in Arctic and sub-Arctic terrains. In these conditions, without clothes, you would be dead in about 15 minutes.

The most effective clothing provides a system of layers that trap warm air to form an effective insulation. If you are caught out in Arctic conditions due to vehicle failure, air-crash etc, improvise layered clothing and insulation.

Warm and windproof

Outer-shell garments should be windproof. Arctic conditions are usually dry, and waterproof outers (unless they are of 'breathing' material such as Goretex) should be avoided, as they cause condensation to build up inside, soaking your inner garments.

Many fabrics lose their insulating efficiency when they are wet. Goose and duck down, very popular in dry-cold outer garments, clump disastrously when wet, losing the 'lofted' air spaces that give them their insulating qualities.

Cotton garments and kapok quilt fittings also become heavy and cold. Wool, on the other hand, functions well when wet, as do a range of modern synthetic materials such as

polyester, which can be woven into single-layered clothing, used as quilting fillers, or processed into thick piles and fleeces which have the added advantage that they 'wick' moisture away from inside layers.

The effort expended in keeping warm should be regulated carefully to avoid overheating and sweating. Chopping a tree down to make a shelter could be a fatal expenditure of energy, burning up vital resources and soaking clothing with perspiration.

Frostbite

The prime dangers of cold-weather conditions are frostbite and hypothermia, as the cold strikes at both the outer and inner body. Your extremities – hands, feet, ears and noses – are particularly susceptible to frostbite, but any exposed skin is at risk, and the risk is multiplied by wind speed.

The wind-chill factor transforms

Keep active, but take your time. Everything takes longer. The cold slows you down, the kit is awkward and the snow exhausts you. As long as you're prepared for that, you can cope.

Preventing frostbite

It is easier to prevent frostbite or to stop it in its early stages than to thaw out and take care of badly-frozen flesh.

1 Wear enough clothing for protection against cold and wind.
2 Clothing and equipment must not restrict the circulation.
3 Do not touch cold metal or oils at extreme low temperatures.
4 Avoid unnecessary exposure to strong winds.
5 Exercise the face, fingers and toes to keep them warm and to detect any signs of numbness.
6 Watch your mate for signs of frostbite; he should do the same for you.
7 Thaw any frozen spots immediately.

modestly-cold temperatures into deadly, tissue-destroying assaults on the body. An 18-mph wind in a 9.5°C temperature results in a −23.3°C wind-chill temperature. At wind-chill temperatures below −6°C, exposed flesh freezes in 60 seconds or less. An ambient temperature (measured by thermometer) of −28.8°C is converted by a 35-mph wind into a deadly −59.4°C wind-chill temperature. At this level, flesh freezes in 30 seconds.

Removing a mitten long enough to undo clothing and urinate can result in frostbitten fingers. Deep frostbite, which can result in lost fingers, toes or even limbs, kills by incapacitating the victim. But gangrene can also easily set in, and that will indeed see you off unless you get medical help.

The first signs of frostbite may be a waxy whiteness on the skin. Keep a close eye on your mates for these

The 'wind chill effect' is a vital point to bear in mind when you're trying to survive in cold conditions. An already cold air temperature combined with a strong, freezing wind can lead to an equivalent chill temperature that may be deadly. This table will help you work out the likely effect of the wind on your body.

WIND CHILL EFFECT

WIND SPEED		TEMPERATURE (°C)																				
CALM	CALM	4	2	1	−4	−7	−9	−12	−15	−18	−20	−23	−26	−29	−31	−34	−37	−40	−43	−45	−48	−51
KNOTS	MPH	EQUIVALENT CHILL TEMPERATURE																				
3-6	5	2	1	−4	−7	−9	−12	−15	−18	−20	−23	−26	−29	−32	−34	−37	−40	−43	−45	−48	−51	−57
7-10	10	1	−7	−9	−12	−15	−18	−23	−26	−29	−32	−37	−40	−43	−45	−51	−54	−57	−59	−62	−68	−70
11-15	15	−4	−9	−12	−18	−20	−23	−29	−32	−34	−40	−43	−45	−51	−54	−57	−62	−65	−68	−73	−76	−79
16-19	20	−7	−12	−15	−18	−23	−26	−32	−34	−37	−43	−45	−51	−54	−59	−62	−65	−70	−73	−79	−82	−84
20-23	25	−9	−12	−18	−20	−26	−29	−34	−37	−43	−45	−51	−54	−59	−62	−68	−70	−76	−79	−84	−87	−93
24-28	30	−12	−15	−18	−23	−29	−32	−34	−40	−45	−48	−54	−57	−62	−65	−70	−73	−79	−82	−87	−90	−95
29-32	35	−12	−15	−20	−23	−29	−34	−37	−40	−45	−51	−54	−59	−62	−68	−73	−76	−82	−84	−90	−93	−98
33-36	40	−12	−18	−20	−26	−29	−34	−37	−43	−48	−51	−57	−59	−65	−70	−73	−79	−82	−87	−90	−95	−101
WINDS ABOVE 40MPH HAVE LITTLE ADDITIONAL EFFECTS		LITTLE DANGER			INCREASING DANGER (Flesh may freeze within 1 minute)					GREAT DANGER (Flesh may freeze within 30 seconds)												
		DANGER OF FREEZING EXPOSED FLESH FOR PROPERLY CLOTHED PERSONS																				

many layers of clothing, you may be unaware that you are losing body moisture. Your heavy clothing absorbs the moisture, which evaporates in the air. You must drink water to replace this loss of fluid. Your need for water is as great when it's cold as when it's hot.

One way to tell if you are becoming dehydrated is to check the colour of your urine in the snow. If it makes the snow dark yellow, you are becoming dehydrated and need to replace body fluids; if the snow turns light yellow or remains normal, you're OK.

There's also a condition called 'cold diuresis', which is an increased output of urine caused by exposure to cold. It decreases body fluids, which must be replaced.

patches. If you are on your own, periodically feel your face and ears for the typical numbness.

If you encounter frostbite, rub snow onto the area until the whiteness or numbness disappears. Alternatively, gently compress the affected area with a warm hand. Do not rub the frostbitten area directly; you are likely to break the skin, leading to an open wound and infection.

Hypothermia

Hypothermia occurs when the temperature of the inner body-core, which houses the vital organs, falls below 35°C. The normal inner body temperature is 36.8°C.

As hypothermia sets in, movements slow up, thought processes are dulled, and you begin to lose co-ordination. You're dying on your feet, though you probably won't know it. Your speech becomes slurred. When your body temperature falls to 25°C and below, death is almost inevitable.

One of the best ways of dealing with hypothermia is to put the victim naked inside a sleeping bag with another person, also naked. A second person can also administer the warm, sweet drinks (such as honey, dextrose, sugar or cocoa) and food necessary for recovery. DO NOT FORCE AN UNCONSCIOUS PERSON TO DRINK.

If you manage to get back to civilisation, the hypothermia victim can be immersed in a warm bath. But start with the trunk area first, otherwise there's a risk of cardiac arrest and shock.

A victim will also need some time to recover, because the attack will have profoundly affected the circulation system.

Trench foot and immersion foot re-

In extreme cold a combatant or evader can become depressed, irritable and indifferent to essential tasks. Stay fit, maintain a determined will to win, and follow the drills. You'll survive.

sult from many hours or days of exposure to wet or damp conditions at a temperature just above freezing. The feet become cold and swollen and have a waxy appearance. Walking becomes difficult, and the feet feel heavy and numb. The nerve and muscles suffer the most damage, but gangrene can also occur in extreme cases, and it may become necessary to have the foot or leg amputated.

The best preventive is to keep the feet dry. Carry extra socks with you in a waterproof packet. Wet socks can be dried against the body. Wash your feet daily and put on dry socks.

In cold weather, bundled up in

Snow blindness

It is vital to protect your eyes in bright sun and snow. Wear your sunglasses. If you don't have any, improvise. Cut slits in a piece of cardboard, thin wood, tree bark or other available material. Putting soot under your eyes will help reduce glare.

Sunburn

Exposed skin can become sunburned even when the air temperature is below freezing: the sun's rays reflect at all angles from snow, ice and water. Extra sensitive areas of skin are

Two degrees of frostbite

Superficial frostbite causes just the skin or the tissue immediately beneath it to turn white or waxy. After rewarming, the area will become numb and mottled and will swell, sting or burn for some time. In more severe cases blisters will occur, drying up to become hard and black. **Deep frostbite** goes down into the tissue, sometimes as far as the bone. It is accompanied by blisters or swellings. The area goes blue, violet or – the worst – grey and can be very painful. In acute deep frostbite the affected area may auto-amputate: in World War II, German soldiers at Stalingrad in Russia sometimes found loose toes rattling about in their boots.

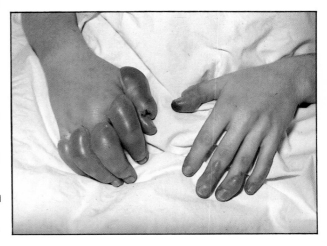

SAS men landed by helicopter on South Georgia during the Falklands war of 1982 came perilously close to freezing to death after a 'whiteout' made flying impossible out on the glacier. The real enemy was the Antarctic weather, not the Argentines.

the lips, nostrils and eyelids. You should apply sunburn cream or lip salve whenever you are out in the sun.

You can get sunburn more easily at high altitudes during the same time of exposure to the sun.

Snow blindness

This is caused by the reflection of ultra-violet rays caused by the sun shining brightly on a snow-covered area. The symptoms of snow blindness are a gritty feeling in the eyes, pain in and over the eyes that increases with eyeball movement, eyes watering and becoming red, and a headache, which intensifies with continued exposure to light.

Prolonged exposure to these rays can result in permanent eye damage. To treat snow blindness, bandage the eyes until the symptoms disappear.

You can prevent snow blindness by wearing sunglasses.

Constipation

If you put off relieving yourself because of the cold, eat dehydrated foods, drink too little liquid and have irregular eating habits, you may become constipated.

Although not disabling, constipation can cause discomfort. Increase your fluid intake to at least two quarts per day and eat fruits, if available, and other foods that will loosen your bowels. Eating burnt wood and charcoal may help!

Making a sleeping bag

If you do not have a sleeping bag, you can make one out of parachute cloth or similar material and natural dry material such as leaves, pine needles or moss. Place the dry material between two layers of parachute cloth.

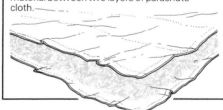

Although washing yourself daily may be impractical and uncomfortable in a cold climate, you must do it. Washing helps to prevent skin rashes that can develop into more serious problems.

In some situations, you may be able to take a snow bath. Take a handful of snow and wash your body where sweat and moisture accumulate, such as under the arms and between the legs, front and rear, and then wipe yourself dry.

If you cannot bathe, periodically wipe yourself dry in these areas. If possible, wash your feet daily and put on clean, dry socks. Change your underwear at least twice a week. If you are unable to wash your underwear, take it off, shake it, and let it air out for an hour or two.

If you are with natives or are using a shelter that has been used before, check your body and clothing each night for lice. If your clothing has become infested, use insecticide powder if you have some. Otherwise, hang your clothes in the cold, then beat and brush them. This will help get rid of the lice, but not their eggs, which will persist in the folds of your clothes.

Trench foot: Curse of the Falklands

Trench foot (or immersion foot) was a common affliction suffered by English and Argentine soldiers during the Falklands campaign. It results from prolonged exposure of the feet to temperatures near (but not necessarily below) freezing.

In the early stages the feet and toes are pale and feel cold, numb and stiff; walking becomes difficult. If preventive action is not taken, the feet will swell and become painful. In extreme cases the flesh dies and amputation of the foot or leg may be necessary.

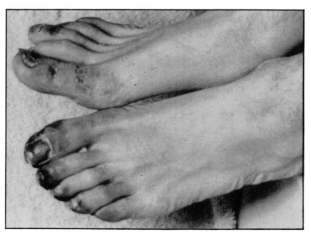

Travel in the Arctic

Deep snow means deep trouble if you're on the move. On foot or in an ordinary vehicle, you've got very little chance unless you've taken precautions beforehand. As well as the difficulty of moving through the snow itself, there are other less obvious things to worry about.

To start with, deep snow will change the appearance of the countryside, turning navigation by map into a nightmare. Secondly, the snow will hide all sorts of obstacles and dangers. Falling into a ditch filled with three metres of soft snow may sound like it could be fun, but the reality is deadly. You would find it very difficult to climb out before you were overcome by exhaustion and died of exposure. That is, unless you drowned in the snow first.

Consider and conserve

So what can you do to make your way through Arctic, sub-Arctic or Alpine conditions?

Firstly, you must stay calm and conserve as much energy and body water as possible. If you're carrying a heavy

load of equipment, weapons and ammunition you'll be unable to travel far if there's more than half a metre of untrodden snow on the ground – even if the country is flat.

You have to spread the weight of your body and your load. The two most usual ways of doing that both have their drawbacks – skis are hard

Swedish Fältjägarna Special Forces on the move deep inside the Arctic Circle. Despite the cold and hostile environment, individual movement and fighting is a vital part of the overall defence strategy.

to control unless you know how and, anyway, are almost impossible to make from the sort of material you'll be able to gather. Snowshoes, the other real way to get about, are very tiring unless you're used to them, but they can be improvised using natural materials.

If you're properly equipped, of course, you'll have both available: skis to use when you're travelling any distance, and snowshoes for use in camp, where there are lots of people about – or in heavy brush or undergrowth, where two metres of ski on each foot would make you a little clumsy!

Ski into battle

A fit, experienced skier can keep up a solid 10 kilometres an hour for days on end, even when carrying a full load of equipment. That's an awful lot more than you could manage on foot, and it requires a lot less effort, so there is much to be said for learning how to do it.

There are two main types of ski: Alpine skis are the shorter of the two types, and have fastenings for both the toe and heel of the boot; cross-country or Nordic skis are longer and narrower, with a hinged fastening at the toe only, so that the heel can be raised. This allows you to do a push/step movement that covers the ground remarkably quickly.

Military cross-country skis

The standard military issue ski is 208 cm long (big by Alpine standards). They have holes in the tips, to allow you to tow them in an improvised sledge, and are grooved at the heel to accept mohair 'climbers'.

To the non-skier it may come as a surprise to learn that you can actually walk uphill wearing skis. Originally, people stuck strips of sealskin onto the soles of their skis, with the pile of the short, stiff hairs pointing backwards. The British Army uses mohair instead, but the effect is the same.

The length of a pair of skis isn't terribly important, but the length of the poles is. They're much longer than the poles used in downhill skiing, coming to just below the shoulder. In the British forces they come in three lengths: 51 inches (130 cm); 54 inches (137 cm); and 58 inches (147 cm). Don't damage the points of your skis. They are intentionally sharp, to allow you to get a purchase on hard ice.

Awareness of avalanches

Avalanches come in four different types:
1 Soft slab: snow fallen on lee slopes which fails to bond with older snow.
2 Hard slab: a deceptively hard surface formed by high winds and cold air temperature.
3 Airborne: new snow falling on an already hard crust.
4 Wet snow: usual in spring thaw, often after a rapid temperature rise.

Some avalanches can reach 200 miles per hour, and carry with them thousands of tonnes of snow, ice and rock debris, burying a victim up to 10 metres below the surface. Here are some basic precautions to keep you away from danger areas:

1 Stay high.
2 Don't ski across rotten snow, new falls or very steep slopes.
3 Don't travel alone, but do keep a safe distance between group members.
4 Stay out of gullies – you never know what will come down from above.
5 Keep a close watch on the temperature, both of the air and of the snow: check them often, especially in the spring. Sudden changes bring about avalanches.
6 Dig pits from time to time to check on the condition of the snow lower down.
7 Watch for recent avalanche signs: they often come in groups.
8 Keep a very, very careful listening watch.

9 Don't assume, because one group's got across, that it is safe: they could have triggered off an avalanche.
10 Avoid convex parts of a slope; this is where fracturing of the slab commonly occurs.
11 Keep below the treeline; it's generally safer.
12 Keep away from slopes of angles of between 30 and 45 degrees, which are often the most dangerous.
13 The deeper the snow, the greater the danger.
14 Avoid new snow; it takes a minimum of 2-3 days to settle.

15 Travel in the early morning before full sun-up.
16 Do not adopt a 'lightning never strikes twice' attitude, or assume that if there's been an avalanche the danger's passed. Avalanches occur in the same place all the time.
17 On ridges, snow accumulates on the lee side in overhanging piles, called cornices. These often extend far out from the ridge and may break loose if stepped on, so do not stray unless you are sure of your ground.

The elite Mountain and Arctic Warfare Cadre of the Royal Marines trains throughout the harsh Norwegian winter. Despite their own and their hosts' professionalism, 16 Norwegian soldiers were killed in a single avalanche in 1986 during a joint exercise.

Crossing a danger area

Do everything you can to stay away from areas that look or feel like they might be about to avalanche. There may come a time, however, when you just have to go through one. Here are some rules that will increase your chances of making it safely – and some hints as to what to do if you get caught:
1 If you have to cross an avalanche area, travel across the slope one at a time.
2 Follow in the same tracks as the man in front of you.
3 Loosen your ski bindings and take your hands out of the loops on your poles.
4 Slip any rucksack straps off your uphill shoulder so that you can ditch it easily.
5 Fasten your smock hood over your nose and mouth to reduce the chances of drowning if you go down in powder snow.
6 Walk downhill; don't ski.
7 Go straight down, not in a traverse.
8 Keep high and stick to concave slopes.

Caught in an avalanche

If you feel or hear an avalanche coming, you must move fast but carefully – a fall now will almost certainly mean your death. Don't panic. If you stay calm you have a good chance of coming out of it unscathed.
1 Ditch your kit.
2 Find out where you are in relation to the avalanche. You may not be in its path. If it's going to miss you, don't move.
3 Look out for your team mates. Remember their positions. You may have to dig them out.
4 Ski away in a steep traverse. Don't go straight down the fall line. The avalanche may be travelling at anything up to 200 miles per hour.
5 If you get caught at the side of an avalanche, dig outwards – it's easier.
6 Make an air space around your nose and mouth, but keep your mouth shut. In a powder avalanche, try to get a cloth over your nose to act as a filter.
7 Determine which way is up and down, perhaps by dribbling.
8 Start digging your way out before the avalanche has time to settle and freeze into position.
9 If you're covered in powder snow, try a swimming motion. Backstroke is the most effective.

Improvising snowshoes

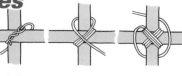

The traditional snowshoe looks a bit like a big tennis racket, but more modern versions are a rounded oblong shape, around 50 cm long and 25 to 30 cm wide, made up of a lightweight frame interlaced with straps of some sort.

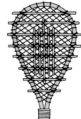

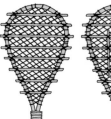

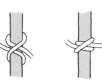

These straps can be made from any suitable material, and so can the frames, which means that at a pinch you can make a pair of snowshoes for yourself. Use stripped straight branches for the frame, and webbing, animal hide cut into strips, or even bark for the cross-straps.

You don't need clever bindings: a single piece of rope, doubled and knotted twice around the foot and ankle, will do fine.

Do not bind the ankle to the snowshoe – allow it to lift in the same way as your heel lifts while walking normally.

Walking at night

In an operational or hostile situation, travel during darkness, unless the weather has closed in sufficiently during the day to hide you in low cloud or fog. Even then, take care; bad weather can lift very quickly, leaving you exposed and unprotected.

And beware travelling in 'whiteout' conditions: the lack of contrasting colours makes it impossible to judge the nature of the terrain. And do not travel during blizzards – they are deadly.

Moving at night can be tricky, as any light from stars and the moon is made even brighter when reflected off the snow.

Plan your moves

Make a plan to work from one feature to another, for shelter and concealment, rather than to trek straight out into open country.

Sounds travels easily in cold climates, so you should keep very quiet and stop to listen every so often.

Always cross a snow bridge at right angles to the obstacle it crosses. Find the strongest part of the bridge by poking ahead with a pole or ice axe. Distribute your weight by crawling or by wearing snowshoes or skis.

Cross streams when the water level is lowest. Normal freezing and thawing action may cause a stream level to vary as much as 2 to 2½ metres per day. This may occur at any time, depending on the distance from a glacier, the temperature, and the terrain. You should also consider this variation in water level when selecting a campsite near a stream.

Choosing your course

Consider rivers, frozen or unfrozen, as avenues of travel. Frozen rivers are frequently clear of loose snow, making travel easier than on the land. Avoid snow covered streams: the snow, which acts as an insulator, may have prevented ice forming over the water.

Your course should be determined by your location and the terrain. In mountainous or wooded areas, it is advisable to follow rivers downstream towards populated areas (Siberia, where rivers flow northward to the high Arctic, is an exception).

When travelling cross-country, try to follow the contour of the land: however, note that valley floors are frequently colder than slopes and ridges, especially at night. Head for a coast, major river, or known point of habitation.

Going the right way

Navigation is tricky in the Arctic. You're near the magnetic pole, so compass readings may be erratic: take more than one, and average them out. Use the shadow tip method or use the sun and stars to show you in which direction north and other points of the compass lie. These techniques will be features in later issues.

Nature itself gives you a few clues:

Crossing thin ice

If you have to cross thin ice, remember these rules:

1 One man at a time.

2 Take your hands out of the loops on your ski poles.

3 Put your equipment over one shoulder only, so you can shrug it off.

3 Loosen the bindings on your skis or snowshoes.

4 Think about distributing your weight by lying flat and crawling.

5 Bear in mind these thicknesses of ice and their corresponding loadbearing capabilities:

5 cm supports 1 man

10 cm supports 2 men side by side

20 cm supports a half-ton vehicle.

If you fall through the ice, get your kit off and up onto the ice; use your poles to help you out. Don't get too close to a team-mate who's fallen through; you'll only end up in there with him. Throw him a line so that you can help him out from a safe distance. Hypothermia will set in very quickly after immersion, so carry out emergency re-warming straight away.

The water is 0°C, and this Royal Marine's body temperature is supposed to be 37°C. So it's only a matter of minutes before the water wins. Unless he gets out he'll collapse when his temperature reaches about 33°C, and die when it gets to 25°C.

The essence of Arctic travel is to get somewhere in a fit state to do a job of work. Pace yourself; work to a steady rhythm, and concentrate. Be in command of the situation – don't let the situation command you.

1 A solitary evergreen tree will always have more growth on its south side.

2 Bark on poplar and birch trees will always be lighter in colour on the south-facing side.

3 Trees and bushes will be bent in the direction that the wind normally blows, so if you know the direction of the prevailing wind you can work out north and south.

4 The snow on the south side of the ridges tends to be more granular than on the north.

5 Snowdrifts usually are on the downwind side of protruding objects like rocks, trees or high banks. By determining the cardinal points of the compass and from them the direction of the drifts, the angle at which you cross them will serve as a check point in maintaining a course.

In the southern hemisphere, of course, the opposite polarity applies.

Pay attention to staying on the right track. You'll get some help in this during clear weather by looking back at your tracks in the snow.

But, of course, that's a sure sign to enemy forces that you're around. You have to be very cunning in the snow to cover up your tracks: stick to the treeline wherever possible, or use existing tracks and patches of broken snow. If you're travelling as a team, keep in each other's tracks.

Be careful how you plant your poles: always put them in the same holes as the guy ahead of you, then the enemy won't know how many there are of you. Alternatively, makes lots of holes to confuse them!

Distance

It's very difficult to judge distances in the Arctic as there are so few visual clues, and the clear air makes estimating distances difficult: they are more frequently underestimated than overestimated.

The simplest way of estimation is to pace out a given distance yourself, but this must be practised to be anywhere near accurate.

Another method is for a rope or some signal wire of a given length (say 50 metres) to be strung between two men. The first man moves off, and when the slack is taken up the first man stops and the second man joins him, then repeats the exercise. Simple mathematics can be used to estimate the distance achieved after a number of repetitions.

Arrive and perform

Your task is to survive and remain fit to carry out your mission. Arriving as a casualty or, even worse, not arriving at all, puts your whole team and operation at risk. So remember the drills.

Emergency Arctic Snow Shelters

You've been separated from your kit, but you've got your first- and second-line survival kit with you. It's a long way to base camp and there's only just over an hour of light left. A light snow is beginning to fall, and the wind's come up, but it's not too bad yet.

You haven't got a tent. You're facing the prospect of a night in the open in worsening conditions. This is an emergency survival situation. Stay calm. Think. You've got a number of options, and you've practised them all. And best of all, you've got your rations!

Shelters made of snow

The simplest way of building a shelter is to use snow. You can make a snow grave, a snow hole or an igloo; all three are better than a tent. Make sure the entrance is lower than the sleeping bench; this will trap the warm air in the living space near the ceiling. Even a burning candle will keep the temperature at about 0°C.

Always smooth off the ceiling to prevent dripping. This, though, will make the shelter airtight, which can lead to lack of oxygen especially if you are using a cooker, so punch a ventilation hole using a ski stick.

Keep a shovel in the shelter to dig yourself out if it blizzards or if the cave collapses; if the temperature is above freezing the snow conditions will not be quite right and the roof may start to fall in. For this reason, don't practise building snow shelters unless it's below freezing point.

Snow trenches

You need about one metre of snow – the deeper the better – into which you dig a simple trench. Make the bottom wider than the top, especially if there are two of you. If it's not quite deep enough, build up a bit at the sides.

Now smooth off the sleeping bench, insulating it with brushwood, if you don't have your sleeping mat with you. Then dig a cold hole next to the door: this acts as a sump for the cold air. Then dig an entrance and move your kit inside, and put the roof on.

This can be tricky, especially if your

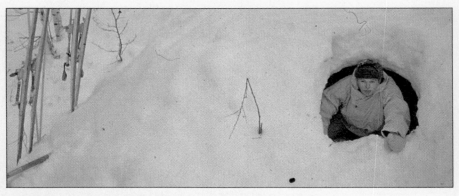

A Marine emerges into daylight from his snow hole. A well-built snow hole is surprisingly warm: a single candle can keep the temperature at about 0°C.

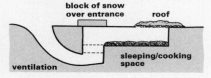

Left: Side view of a snow grave. Dig a trench, then make a tunnel from one end running back to the surface. This provides ventilation and traps cold air. Roof over the trench using your skis and a poncho (this is easier if the trench is narrower at the top than the bottom).

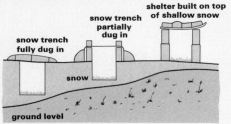

If the snow is too shallow to dig a snow grave or snow hole, you can make an effective shelter by building walls of snow and putting a roof on top.

trench is too wide. The simplest way, if the snow is compact, is to cut blocks and place them over the top, then add more snow. If you find you need support for the snow blocks, use brushwood or tentsheets. You can use skis, but only as a last resort: if you do, put them in upside down, as this helps to stop them freezing in. Then add more snow.

Snow hole or snow cave

If there are two or more of you, you need a large bank or drift of snow, about three metres wide and two metres deep. An avalanche probe will come in handy to gauge the depth. Put on waterproofs if you have them, as you will get wet.

There are two methods of digging: the tunnel method, and the block and cave method. The latter can be used when the snow is compact enough to be cut in blocks. Dig along the full length of the intended cave, using as many men as will fit, while one digs the entrance off to the side.

Once you have dug the sleeping benches, build up the open side of the cave with the excavated snowblocks until it is sealed in. Only the entrance remains open.

Using the tunnel method, only one man can work until the building of the sleeping benches is started; it therefore takes much longer than the block and cave method.

Snow house (igloo)

The igloo – the traditional home of the Eskimo – needs experience and practice to build, and snow must be of the right quality to cut into blocks. Loose snow is useless; and the more granular it is, the smaller the igloo must be.

Work from the inside, cutting out the centre and using your carefully cut blocks to form the base of the wall. Work progressively upwards in a

Here the snow is too shallow to allow a proper snow hole to be dug, so the troops have dug down as far as they can then piled snow up to form the walls and roof. An avalanche pole is useful to judge the snow depth and, therefore, what type of shelter you can build.

Living in snow shelters

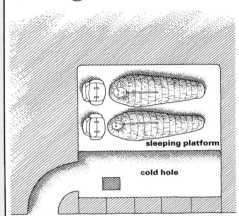

Follow these rules for safety and comfort.

1 Strip off to avoid sweating; the sweat may freeze later. But wear waterproofs when digging or you will get soaked.
2 Make sure your shelter is adequately ventilated at all times.
3 Mark the entrance to your shelter so that you can always find it. This will also help rescuers if the cave collapses.
4 Brush loose snow from yourselves before entering. This prevents damp developing on your clothing in the warm interior of the shelter.
5 Take all your equipment in, ESPECIALLY a shovel.
6 Remove wet clothing and try to dry it overnight.
7 Take your boots into your sleeping bag and keep them near your stomach area. This will help to dry them.
8 Don't boil water for too long; its vapour will cause condensation and dampness.
9 Keep a candle burning to give light and warmth – but keep watch on it.

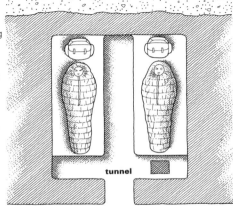

Block and cave method (top view)
The men sleep together on the raised sleeping platform, taking advantage of shared bodily warmth.

Tunnel method (top view)
You can build a raised sleeping platform to one side of the trench or, in this case, on both sides. Until the sleeping platforms are begun, only one man at a time can work in the tunnel.

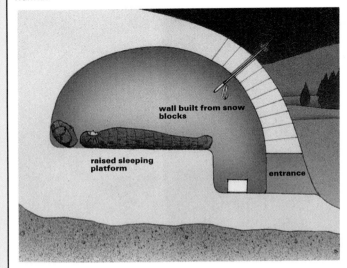

Block and cave method (side view)
You can dig along the full length of the intended cave using as many men as will fit, while one man digs the entrance off to one side. Then seal up the open side with blocks of snow.

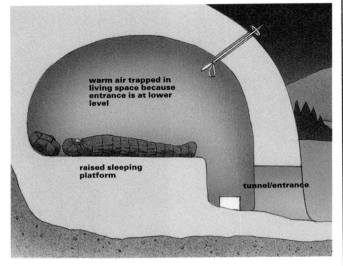

Tunnel method (side view)
Because only one man can work at one time, this takes a lot longer to build. Note the ski pole in the roof to keep a hole open for ventilation. If you forget this the atmosphere can soon become stifling.

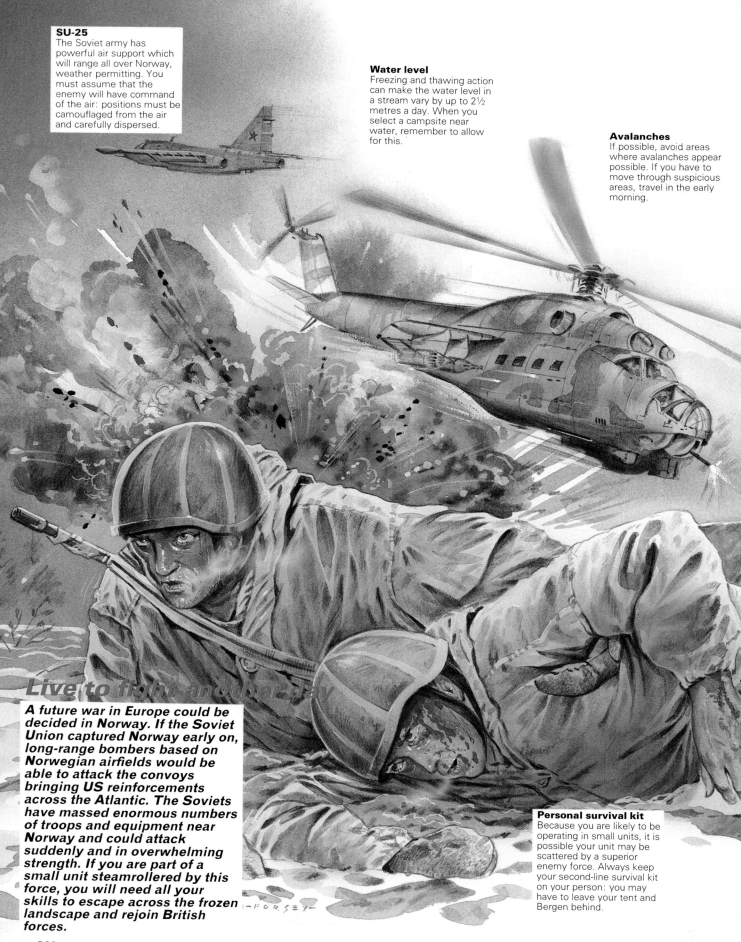

SU-25
The Soviet army has powerful air support which will range all over Norway, weather permitting. You must assume that the enemy will have command of the air: positions must be camouflaged from the air and carefully dispersed.

Water level
Freezing and thawing action can make the water level in a stream vary by up to 2½ metres a day. When you select a campsite near water, remember to allow for this.

Avalanches
If possible, avoid areas where avalanches appear possible. If you have to move through suspicious areas, travel in the early morning.

Live to fight another day

A future war in Europe could be decided in Norway. If the Soviet Union captured Norway early on, long-range bombers based on Norwegian airfields would be able to attack the convoys bringing US reinforcements across the Atlantic. The Soviets have massed enormous numbers of troops and equipment near Norway and could attack suddenly and in overwhelming strength. If you are part of a small unit steamrollered by this force, you will need all your skills to escape across the frozen landscape and rejoin British forces.

Personal survival kit
Because you are likely to be operating in small units, it is possible your unit may be scattered by a superior enemy force. Always keep your second-line survival kit on your person: you may have to leave your tent and Bergen behind.

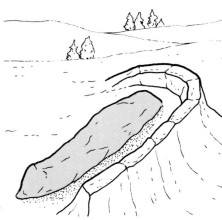

Snow wall

If you cannot build a proper snow hole or shelter, you can shelter behind a semi-circular wall. At least this will keep you out of the wind and perhaps allow you to cook something.

spiral, shaping the blocks as you go, and leaning them just slightly further inwards with each spiral. Finally a key block is inserted – carefully – either by widening the centre hole or trimming the key block until it drops gently into place. The wall should be chest to shoulder high.

Finally, build an S-shaped tunnel away from the prevailing wind. In deep snow, this can be underground. Construct sleeping benches inside, and fill in any holes in the walls with loose snow.

Snow wall

In dire emergency, a simple semi-circular snow wall will keep the worst of the weather at bay and provide shelter from the wind, allowing you to cook and sleep for a limited period.

These are your options. You will find a snowhole rather oppressive at first, but it is the most comfortable and warm form of shelter in the Arctic and much preferred by Arctic troops.

Wear waterproof trousers when shovelling, and remember to keep your shovel inside the shelter in case you have to dig yourself out after a blizzard or the shelter collapses.

Ridges

On ridges, snow accumulates on the lee side until it forms an overhang called a cornice. Cornices can extend far out from the top of the ridge but can break loose if you step on them.

Snow walls

These give cover from observation at ground level, but they cast a telltale shadow which will betray your presence to any passing 'Hind' gunship. Build trenches with good overhead cover and keep movement around your position to a minimum.

Deep snow

It is almost impossible to travel in deep snow, without skis or snowshoes, and travelling by foot leaves a clearly-marked trail for any pursuers to follow.

Streams

Avoid snow-covered streams if you can. The snow which acts as an insulator may have prevented ice forming, and you could end up immersed in very cold water.

Escape motivation

If you are taken prisoner you might get a chance to practise your Arctic survival skills in Siberia. So it is worth making the effort to get away, even it it means a solo trip across Norway.

Visibility

Remember that in the clear Arctic air you are likely to underestimate distances. By contrast, in 'white out' conditions you will not be able to judge the nature of the terrain, so stay put.

What it takes to be a Combat Infantryman

BASIC TRAINING

The Light Infantry

The Royal Green Jackets

The Light Division combines the Light Infantry and Rifle Regiments, which were the elite formations of the British Army during the Napoleonic Wars. The dark green beret harks back to the green rifleman's uniform originally introduced when the rest of the infantry still wore conspicuous red coats.

Gone are the days when all you had to learn to become a combat infantryman in the British Army was how to fire a rifle and how to drill on the square. Today's infantryman is a complete professional, and you need every minute of the 19-week training course to come up to the modern army's exacting standards. But at the end of that time you'll be an expert in your craft.

Your combat infantry training is divided into six phases:

Weeks 1-6 Basic training
Weeks 7-10 Weapon training and fieldcraft
Week 11 First battle camp
Weeks 12-15 Consolidation
Weeks 16-18 Field firing, final battle camp
Week 19 Passing-out parade

Toughening up

This first six weeks at an infantry depot can be a shock to the system: however tough or fit you think you are when you arrive, you soon discover that you are not 'army fit'. You've been wearing trainers all your life, but you can't go to war in trainers: so you have to learn to operate in a pair of 'Boots Combat High'. These were introduced after the Falklands War because of the damage done to infantrymen's feet by the old boot.

The new boots are a good bit of kit, but they take some breaking in. The road runs are the real killers. But you get used to the boots, and the exercise, and as the weeks go by you can see and feel the weight coming off and the muscles appearing.

Then there's the drill. It seems a waste of time at first but you start to get it together with the rest of the platoon and it begins to feel good. At first you're all arms and legs. The platoon sergeant screams orders at long range while two or three corporals run around like a pack of hounds, pouncing on every mistake.

Firing the SA80

Before inserting a new magazine you must apply the safety catch. This is a transverse bar above the trigger which you push to make the weapon safe.

Fighting with the SA80

The modern infantryman needs to master a wide range of skills if he is to survive in combat. Here a recruit practices individual fire and manoeuvre with the SA80 rifle.

Grouping your shots

You are introduced to your rifle at the beginning of your training. To get any further, you must learn to shoot consistently, placing your shots as close together as you can.

The SA80 fires one shot per squeeze of the trigger when set at 'R' (Repetition) as seen here. You should only switch to 'A' (Automatic) during close-quarter fighting.

Having inserted a fresh magazine, cock the weapon by pulling the cocking handle smartly to the rear. Keep your finger away from the trigger, otherwise you may shoot accidentally.

Ready to fire, you now release the safety catch by pushing the bar in from the other side.

The SA80 5.56-mm rifle is the personal weapon of the majority of British infantrymen: it is certainly the weapon on which all infantrymen first qualify when they are in training. The issue programme of the weapon commenced in earnest in early 1987, though certain units were issued with the weapon much earlier than this as part of the trials programme.

The SA80 is a gas-operated assault rifle with a single-shot and automatic facility. It has a magazine holding 30 rounds, a muzzle velocity of 940 metres per second, and an all-up weight, including the SUSAT optical sight and a full magazine, of 5.08 kg. The weapon is 780 mm long without bayonet, and 980 mm long with bayonet fixed. The range settings using the SUSAT optical sight are from 300 to 800 metres, and the most effective battle range of the weapon is up to 400 metres. SUSAT (Sight Unit Small Arms Trilux) has a magnification of ×4 and a field of view of 177 mils. There is, in addition, an iron sight.

You are required to produce different types of fire with the SA80. In battle you will normally carry six full magazines of ammunition, one on your weapon and five in your pouches. In addition you will be issued with a bandolier containing a further 150 rounds, used to supply the Light Support Weapons (LSWs) or refuel your own magazines during a lull in the battle. You may also be required to carry some tracer ammunition for the LSWs or for target indication. The types of fire used in battle are:

1 Deliberate fire
This is a steady rate of fire of, normally, not more than 10 rounds per minute. It is generally ordered after a fire fight has been won, in order to prevent the enemy returning aimed fire, moving their positions or observing you.

2 Snapshooting
This is intermittent, opportunity-shooting at enemy who show themselves for short periods.

3 Rapid fire
This is used to win a fire fight or when the enemy are assaulting your position. With practice, you will be able to achieve 20 aimed shots per minute at different targets.

4 Automatic fire
This is normally only used in close-quarter battle, particularly during the final stages of an assault, in an ambush, in house clearing operations, when clearing trenches, bunkers or woods and when repelling a mass attack. Its use must be carefully controlled in order to conserve ammunition.

In operational conditions it is often impossible to engage targets while lying down because of undergrowth, crops, or cover in streets and buildings, so you must learn to fire the SA80 while kneeling, sitting, squatting or standing.

The highly sophisticated sling allows 'hands off' carriage of the weapon, either across the front of your body or with the muzzle pointing at the ground by your side. If a higher state of readiness is required, you should operate the sling quick-release buckle which allows you to bring the weapon up across the body, with your left hand on the hand guard and right hand around the pistol grip with the barrel pointing upwards in the 'High Port' position. This position is used when going through scrub or crossing obstacles. If you stumble, the muzzle of your SA80 will not get entangled or filled with dirt or point at your comrades.

Hitting a static target with the SA80 is relatively straightforward. The tip of the upright pointer in the SUSAT sight is placed at the base of the target you are aiming at. However, most shots fired under operational conditions will be at short ranges against moving targets. The enemy is likely to move quickly from cover to cover and will show himself for the shortest possible periods of time. You must therefore learn to anticipate the enemy's movements, so when you fire at a moving target, because the target continues to move during the time of flight of the bullet you should aim in front of the target, otherwise the shots will fall behind it.

Obviously the amount of 'lead' you give the target will depend on its speed, range and direction of movement: a running man will require more lead than a man walking, and a target moving obliquely across your front will require less lead than a target crossing directly at right angles to you. Also, the further away the target, the greater the lead it requires. You can only gauge the correct amount of lead for different targets after much experience: it is a matter of 'feel'.

The kneeling, supported position. You shoot from a variety of stances to see how your grouping is affected by your firing position.

When firing from the sitting position, you must keep your elbows inside your knees and your legs either straight like this or crossed. You must be at 45° to the target.

You fire five rounds from the prone position at the bottom centre of each white marker from 25 metres. Here the instructor measures the size of your group.

Meet your weapons

During that first six weeks you start getting to know your personal weapon, the SA80. This is one of six main weapons that you will become expert in handling during your training. These are the SA80, the Light Support Weapon (LSW), the General Purpose Machine Gun (GPMG), the 66-mm Light Anti-Tank Weapon (LAW), the 84-mm Medium Anti-Tank Weapon (MAW) and the L2 Grenade. You learn about these weapons progressively through your training,

but it's mostly the SA80 in the first six weeks.

You've got to be able to handle it in every situation: fire it standing, kneeling, sitting and lying; strip it blindfolded and put it back together again – because you may have to clean it in the dark; adjust the sights and adjust the gas setting; fire it on automatic or single shots, using the iron sight or the SUSAT sight, with or without bayonet. You've got to be professional – really professional. That's the only way you'll win in battle.

Training camp

You practise a lot of what you've learned about the SA80, basic fieldcraft, section drills, judging distance, camouflage, duties of a sentry, and many of the other bits of basic knowledge that you have to take in during the first six weeks, at a training camp, away from the depot. This is not a battle camp, but 10 days away in a different environment. You need the change of scene badly, and you need to get out into the field. That's what proper infantry soldiering is about.

The SUSAT sight

The SUSAT sight is an invaluable aid to accurate shooting. Providing you with ×4 magnification, it is especially useful in bad light, but your immediate field of vision is limited and you must remember where your mates are when you are shooting.

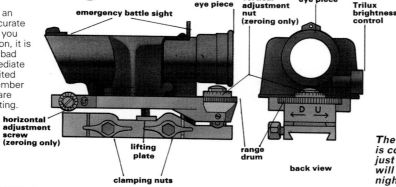

emergency battle sight · eye piece · vertical adjustment nut (zeroing only) · eye piece · Trilux brightness control · horizontal adjustment screw (zeroing only) · lifting plate · range drum · clamping nuts · back view

The sight picture on SUSAT: if your rifle is correctly zeroed the shot will impact just above the point of the arrow. The tip will illuminate when you are shooting at night.

SA80 bayonet and zeroing

The bayonet on the SA80 is unusual. The bayonet itself is shaped to produce good penetration when thrust point-first into the body, and is designed to part the ribs without embedding into the bone. It incorporates a blade for sawing wood, a sharpening stone, wire cutters and a bottle opener.

Also, the handle is shaped so that, if it is removed from the rifle, it can be used as a fighting knife. As well as learning to strip, handle and shoot the SA80, you will also be taught

bayonet fighting drills. However advanced warfare becomes, there will always be circumstances in which the infantryman has to close with the enemy and kill him. If your magazine is empty, it may be that your only method of self-defence is to use your bayonet.

The SA80 has to be zeroed to each individual like any other rifle. Zeroing is a personal thing, and it is most unusual for any two people to have exactly the same zero with the same weapon. Everyone aims slightly differently, and

is affected differently by the so called 'jump' of the weapon before the bullet leaves the barrel. The extent of 'jump' is influenced by the build of the firer, his firing position and the tightness of his hold. To zero the SA80 a series of five-round groups are fired at a target from a distance of 100 metres. The Mean Point of Impact (MPI) is calculated and the SUSAT adjusted according to a set of guidelines to bring the MPI up or down or left or right. This process is continued until the rifle is firing at the centre of the target.

The SA80 is an outstanding weapon. It is robust, relatively simple to operate and maintain and it is accurate and effective. The British Army is now the proud possessor of the best assault rifle in the world.

The SA-80 bayonet with two scabbards showing (left) the sharpener on one side, and (right) the fold-away saw.

The bayonet and scabbard fit together to make a handy pair of wire-cutters. The bayonet is balanced to be used in the hand as well as on the rifle.

The saw is useful for cutting wood when you are building a basha or making camouflage poles.

The scabbard has a sharpening block fitted to it, so you have no excuse for having a dull blade.

Combat Report
Malaysia:
'Hearts and Minds' Part 2

A former member of the SAS Regiment continues his account of SAS operations on the border between Borneo and Indonesia. By 1968 the Indonesians had officially given up sending their soldiers over the border, but the true picture was rather different.

The second time I saw action wasn't quite so lighthearted.

The boss and three of the minders had vanished off to take a look at a suspected terrorist camp about 20 klicks away. There was a lot of swamp, thick jungle and a few steep hills on the way, so we thought they'd be away for about four or five days.

On the morning of the second day, the headman of the local village came rushing up and started chattering away to Moh, our interpreter. Actually, the interpreter was on loan from the Feds (Malaysian Forces) but he was a bloody ace guy, a good soldier and a good mate to all of us – he invited us to his wedding a few months later, and I seem to remember that the boss ended up engaged (although only for the night) to old Moh's sister!

The headman had heard that a small party of very bad men were heading towards us down the track – one that led into the jungle for about five klicks until coming to an abandoned village. 'Bad men' can mean anything to the Aborigines, anything from terrorists to missionaries who want them to stop worshipping butterflies. Still, our remaining minder figured not to take any chances. We persuaded the headman to take his people, about 30 in all, off on a long hike. Then we set up an ambush.

Into the killing ground

The signaller was actually Royal Sigs, and knew his job. I'd done a few courses and, in theory, knew mine. The medic was a little concerned, muttering something about saving lives and not taking them, but the minder explained that since he was British Army he was a soldier anyway and the choice was between getting involved or getting hurt. By the minder. Not much of a choice, really. As for old Moh, he couldn't wait to get stuck in. Don't misunderstand me; we did actually have a pretty good idea of what we were doing. It's just that the minders knew it all a little bit better.

The minder went up the trail to find an ambush site. These had all been figured out as soon as we moved into the village, but I think he was looking for as foolproof a place as possible.

A few minutes later, the minder came back and took us to our positions. He took the GPMG for himself, assigned the other two guys, and gave me the point spot – where you let the enemy move past you, into the killing ground, and take them out if they try to escape back up the track. And for this I had an SLR – more stopping power than an Armalite – and a shotgun.

They were terrorists

I inched into my position, breathing a silent prayer that all the snakes and scorpions had gone on holiday, concealed myself, and waited. I'll never forget how alive I felt then. It's a cliche; it's been said many, many times before; but everything does become more intense before and during combat. I could smell all the smells from the village about a mile down the track – not just woodsmoke, but the faint, sweet smell of evaporated milk diluted with water that we used to drink. I could hear every sound in the jungle . . . so much so that when I heard a gentle scratching sound just off to one side of my head, I looked carefully around and realised that I was listening to ants walking on leaves.

We suspected that a terrorist group was still lurking in the jungle about 12 miles away. The group we ambushed came from an abandoned village much nearer.

It was sound – or lack of it – that told me someone was coming down the track. First, a noisy screeching as the birds and monkeys gave the alarm. Then, silence. Absolute silence – except for the ants, who had just discovered my left leg and had summoned all their friends and relatives to have a taste.

When four men came in sight it was obvious to me, at least, that they were terrorists. Firstly, they were moving in file formation, 10 metres between each man. Secondly, they were carrying Armalites and grenades. No chance that they were simply hunters. No chance that they were Feds (all Federal operations were banned in a 'hearts and minds' operation area). I shrunk into myself, felt my testicles contract and breathed very, very slowly. They seemed to take hours to walk past my position . . . and as the last man moved out of my field of vision, I inched my SLR (safety off, round in the chamber) to follow them down the track.

Firing on full automatic

The next sound I heard was the GPMG firing a ten-second burst. Then a pause. Then a five-second burst. Then the sound of someone running back up the track towards me. Then the sound of an Armalite firing on full automatic – and then the last terrorist that had gone down the track burst into view, running for his life and spraying the jungle in all directions with .223 rounds.

If he hadn't been firing, I might have been tempted to let him go so that he could carry back an Awful Warning to his buddies across the border. As it was, I reckoned that there was a good chance a round could hit me, so I sighted on his upper body and fired.

An SLR does have good stopping power. I got two rounds into him, and that spun him across the track and into a tree trunk, where he slid to the ground. Then there was total silence, broken by the minder shouting out for everyone to stay where they were and to keep the apparently dead men covered. I waited for what seemed like hours, until the minder came in sight with Moh. Moh was checking each terrorist while the minder covered him.

We took what documents they had, plus their weapons, which would be quietly destroyed later. The bodies were taken deep into the jungle and buried. No official account of that incident was ever made. How could it? After all, officially the terrorists didn't exist.

Soldiers from 2 Para on patrol during intensive jungle training in Malaysia after British troops reinforced the Federal forces in case of a major Indonesian attack. Our terrorist incident went unreported since the terrorist problem had officially ceased to exist since then.

What it takes to be a Combat Infantryman
WEAPON TRAINING

The Light Infantry

The Royal Green Jackets

The old and the new: The GPMG (top) compared with the LSW (bottom) and the new FN Minimi (middle), which has the advantage of magazine or belt feed.

Basic training complete, and a long weekend of relaxation over, you find you've got to get down to some concentrated learning during the next four-week phase of your training. You may be wearing your Green Beret now, but you're still not an expert at anything – and there are many subjects you haven't even started to learn.

Before you go to first battle camp in Week 11, you've got to learn about section battle drills, ambushes, OPs, patrol base camps and recce and fighting patrols. You've got to become an expert with the SA80, and be able to fire it safely on the range. Then, just as you think you've cracked the SA80, your corporal introduces the Light Support Weapon (LSW) to you. It's like the SA80, but it's got a longer barrel and it's mounted on a bipod.

More than anything else, though, this second phase of your training is about rangework. You spend about two days a week on the range. You start by 'zeroing' your SA80 on the 30 metre range. This means adjusting your sights laterally and vertically until the rifle is shooting straight for you. Once you have zeroed your rifle, it becomes your personal weapon.

On the range

It's taken weeks of lessons in skill-at-arms for you to be able to fire the SA80 live. You are handling probably the most lethal assault rifle in the world; your corporal has to be sure that you know what you're doing before he lets you fire live rounds on the range.

When you've zeroed your rifle, you must learn to 'group'. That is, to select a consistent point of aim and put all your rounds on the same part of the target. It's no good shooting all over the place.

The Light Support Weapon is a good deal easier to use and carry than the GPMG, but the LSW is not general-purpose: you cannot put it on a tripod and spray 5.56 mm out to 1800 metres. Out to 800 metres, however, it is a very accurate performer.

Light Support Weapon

The Light Support Weapon or LSW is the successor to the GPMG, and is essentially the same weapon as the SA80 with the same working parts. It differs in a very few respects: its muzzle velocity is 970 rather than 940 metres per second; it weighs 6.88kg rather than 5.08kg including the SUSAT and a full magazine; the barrel length is 900mm rather than 780mm; and it has a bipod.

Like the SA80, the LSW can fire single rounds or bursts. When firing single rounds, your left hand doesn't need to come into contact with the weapon: the bipod can be placed under the gun or resting on the right forearm.

When you are firing bursts, though, the LSW has a tendency to twist to the right even when resting on the bipod. To counteract this you should make sure the butt strap is in firm contact with the top of the shoulder. You do this by pulling directly to the rear with a firm right-hand grip. Your left hand should grip the rear pistol grip, with the heel of the hand against the left side of the grip. Keep your wrist rigid so that the weapon is prevented from rotating.

Adjustments in elevation are achieved by moving your elbows inwards or outwards, though major adjustments can only be achieved by altering the bipod height. Adjustments for direction in the prone position mean more body and leg re-adjustment than with the SA80.

The LSW can also be fired as a rifle (that is, with the bipod folded), but remember that the point of balance will be further forward due to the longer barrel and to the bipod: you must maintain a very firm grip with your left hand.

The LSW is designed primarily to produce rapid fire for the section when required. When you are conducting an ambush or are in a defensive position facing massed infantry attack, the requirement for up to 60 rounds a minute can only be met by automatic fire and efficient magazine changing.

During sustained rapid firing the chamber, barrel and trigger of the LSW will become very hot. The weapon is air cooled, so during lulls in the battle you should cock the weapon and hold it open to allow the chamber to cool.

You are likely to engage targets at longer ranges with the LSW than the SA80, so you must learn the theory of 'aiming off'. The LSW gunner must be prepared to produce effective fire up to 800 metres: as the range increases, so does the distance into wind that you must fire to correct its effect on the bullets fired. As a guide, assuming a fresh direct crossing wind, the LSW gunner must aim off into wind as follows:

Range	Displacement (mm)	Point of aim on man-sized target
100 m	19	Nil
200 m	69	½ way centre to edge
300 m	158	½ way centre to edge
400 m	272	edge of target
500 m	438	1 target width
600 m	717	1½ targets' width
700 m	-	2 targets' width
800 m	-	4 targets' width

You do, however, have the advantage of extra tracer rounds in your magazine that will help your observation of the effect of wind on your shots.

The new organisation for a section, when the introduction of SA80 and LSW is complete, is six riflemen armed with SA80 and two gunners armed with LSW. This allows the section to operate with two equally-balanced fire teams of three riflemen and one LSW gunner, or with one assault team of section commander and four or

The Enfield Weapon System: how it works

The SA80 is essentially the same as the Armalite AR18, having the same gas piston and rotary bolt.

Spent brass tumbles from the ejection port as an LSW fires down a 600-metre range. It's accuracy at this range is incredible for a 5.56-mm weapon, but it is almost too accurate. A light machine-gun is sometimes required to produce a wide pattern of fire to suppress an enemy unit, but the LSW tends to produce a tight group.

1 Action cocked.
Bolt locked, ready to fire. The bolt head has a ring of lugs which pass through and rotate to lock up against a similar ring of 'teeth' protruding from the chamber, known as the barrel extension.

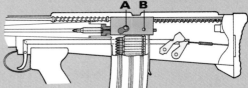

2 Action firing.
Safety catch off. Squeezing the trigger releases the hammer via a transfer bar. The hammer hits the base of the firing pin, which in turn strikes the percussion cap on the base of the round. The firing pin is secured in the bolt and bolt carrier by pin 'B'.

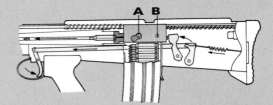

3 Cartridge ignition
The percussion cap ignites the powder in the cartridge and propels the bullet down the barrel. The expanding gases behind the bullet vent through the gas port in the barrel near the muzzle, and force the gas piston rod back against the bolt carrier. Extra gas is bled off through holes in the gas regulator once the piston is moving.

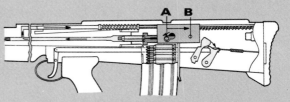

4 Action unlocking
The bolt carrier is forced back against the pressure of the main spring. cocking the hammer as it moves back along the guide rods. The bolt is secured to the bolt carrier by a pin. **'A'**, which rotates the bolt by moving into a groove on the side of the receiver, when the carrier moves back.

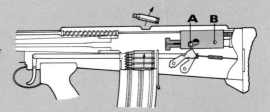

5 Ejection and reloading
The bolt rotates and moves through the gap in the teeth of the barrel extension, extracting and ejecting the empty case to the right. The mainspring forces the bolt forward, stripping a round out of the magazine and chambering it. Pin **'A'** moves up in the slot in the bolt carrier to lock the bolt by rotating it ready for the next shot.

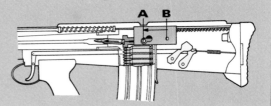

The LSW can produce exceptionally accurate fire support, and the section commander can call for either 'rapid fire' semi-auto or 'bursts rapid fire' full auto, which helps conserve ammo. Remember that you cannot change the barrel and the weapon fires from a closed bolt, so keep the burst length short and lock the bolt open whenever possible to avoid 'cook off': the heat generated during rapid fire can sometimes cause a spontaneous discharge.

Next you graduate to the 600 metre range, where your shooting practices get progressively more difficult: you start in the 'prone' position, then you learn to shoot standing, sitting and kneeling. You fire at 'snap' targets and take part in 'run downs' – starting at 400 metres, then running to the next firing point at 300 metres and firing so many rounds within a time limit, then to 200 and finally to 100. You do much the same with the LSW – only you start your 'run downs' from 600 metres!

Reassuring instruction

On the range you realise just how professional the corporals are. They coach you, advise you, point out your faults. Their manner changes. The shouting and screaming on the drill square becomes an urgent, efficient, but quiet monotone. It's reassuring, it's encouraging – and you learn.

Racing finish

It's at about this stage that those who are not going to make it – or who didn't want to make it – start to wobble. If you are over 18 when you enlist you have until week 12 of your training to exercise your option to leave the army if you don't like it. So some go – because it's too tough, or they miss their girlfriend, or they just don't like getting up early! When they've gone you can really get down to business, because those who are left really want to be combat infantrymen. And you need to be keen to survive first battle camp in Week 11.

Speedloading

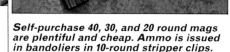

Magazine feed has some advantages over belt feed, but serious firepower is not one of them. You have six 30-round mags and then you will have to start speedloading from your bandolier.

Self-purchase 40, 30, and 20 round mags are plentiful and cheap. Ammo is issued in bandoliers in 10-round stripper clips.

A mag can be reloaded in seconds using stripper clip and guide. One-push equal pressure is the method.

Check that the rounds are correctly seated in the magazine to avoid stoppages.

When loading, push the mag straight in (unlike the SLR), and check the safety and select lever.

five riflemen supported by a fire team of two LSWs, with or without the section second-in-command controlling their fire.

Obviously there are further combinations. In any case, the task of the LSW gunner is to provide fire support to the riflemen in his fire team or, in conjunction with the other section LSW gunner, to the rest of the section. In order to achieve this, each LSW gunner will carry 10 magazines of 30 rounds, one in five of which will be tracer. In addition, each gunner is issued with one bandolier of 150 rounds which he slings over his shoulder or wraps around his waist.

Your training with the LSW will be progressive. First you will carry out an introductory shoot at 25 metres, simply getting the feel of the weapon. Then you will fire a grouping practice at 100 metres before zeroing the weapon – in exactly the same way as you did with the SA80.

You will then carry out a series of firing practices at 200, 300 and 400 metres, and later at 500 and 600 metres. These practices include single-round shooting and timed bursts of fire. Although the weapon is effective up to 800 metres, you will only fire at this range on a Field Firing Range – open countryside where live firing is permitted.

You will find that it's easier to get to grips with the LSW than the SA80. When you start on the SA80 it is a totally new experience: by the time you get to the LSW you can build on your previous experience.

It is important that the whole section is proficient with the LSW, providing maximum flexibility in the event of injury to the two gunners. LSW is less cumbersome than the GPMG; it is certainly lighter, and there are two of them replacing only one GPMG. There is no doubt that the SA80 and the LSW are a winning combination.